MW00560779

Fumbling Towards Repair: A Workbook for Community Accountability Facilitators
by Mariame Kaba and Shira Hassan

Illustrated and Designed by Molly Costello and Rachel Hoffman

June 2019

Published by Project NIA and Just Practice.

Printed in Canada

Table of Contents

AREA 1: Key Frameworks That Inform This Work
Pages 1-40

AREA 2: Food for Thought in Facilitating CA Processes
Pages 41-120

- Section A: Assessing Yourself, Your Capacity, and Your Skills (Pages 46-62)
- Section B: Vexing and Consistent Issues in CA Processes (Pages 63-102)
- Section C: Technical Nuts and Bolts of CA Processes (Pages 103-120)

AREA 3: Useful Activities to Try on Your Own, with Your Team, and with CA Participants
Pages 121-155

- Section A: Activities for Facilitators (Pages 122-127)
- Section B: Activities to Do with Survivors and People Who Caused Harm (Pages 128-146)
- Section C: Team-Building Activities (Pages 147-155)

Resources
Pages 156-160

Label Key

Many pages in this book have **colorful top banners** identifying their content. These pages were designed to: be easily referenced while going through the workbook, be removed from the workbook to share with ease, *and/or* for you to use (write/draw etc.).

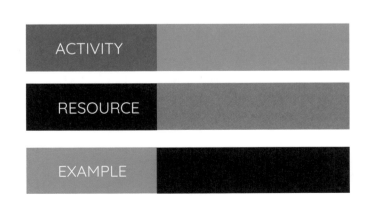

Small Seeds
by Mia Mingus

Many people think that the stories I'm collecting will be huge, sweeping success stories. Stories where everything turns out good and everyone is safe, healed, accountable and forgiven. Stories where "justice" is as clear as the Caribbean water I grew up next to. Where everything works out for the best, leaving an easy road map to follow.

And while these stories, though harder to find, certainly exist, the majority of the stories I am finding are not full-blown success stories, but rather complicated stories of saturated heartbreak and nagging hope, with small victories scattered throughout.

Small victories. The moments that don't seem like much, but stand in stark contrast against the backdrop of the overwhelming isolation, denial and silence that colors most work to address child sexual abuse. Though it can be hard, it is important to acknowledge the small victories and successes within our stories. Small victories mean something, and should not be swept under the rug or minimized.

After spending my life as a child and youth growing up around direct service work to address domestic and sexual violence, and then later as an adult doing transformative justice work to end child sexual abuse (CSA), I know that small victories mean a lot. They are the small seeds we can harvest to plant for the next season and collect again and again, yielding a crop that can withstand the climate that surrounds child sexual abuse.

After over a decade of working to build transformative community responses to child sexual abuse, I know that small victories can have the greatest impact and continue to be our markers of progress. They are small guideposts that we can use to get through the worst of the storm. A compass for where we want to go next.

And even calling them "small" is misleading because, given the current landscape of child sexual abuse, they are no small feat.

When CSA survivors disclose their abuse, especially while they are still young, and are believed—that is a small victory in a world where most survivors of sexual violence are not believed at all when they come forward.

When a family or a family member not only believes a survivor's account of their abuse, but also supports them against the backlash that frequently comes from relatives, friends and/or communities—that is a small victory in a world where many survivors face such backlash on their own.

When an abuser acknowledges the abuse they've done—that is a small victory in a world where so many abusers deny the violence they've done, or, worse, place the blame on survivors and bystanders.

These small victories may seem insignificant to those outside of this work—I get it. The longing inside of us for large-scale change is very real and important, especially in the face of so much fear and unbelievable violence against the most vulnerable members of our communities. Sometimes, I think about it as an ecosystem. If you've never seen the desert, you might think there is little to no life amidst the dry sand and rocks. But those who live there have learned to recognize all the many different kinds of life that exist in the landscape. They have learned to not only wait for the occasional rain to fall from the sky, but also to find water in many different forms—forms that are not always recognizable to others.

This is how I think about small victories in this work. The longer you are part of the work, the more you begin to understand that the downpours that soak through the ground are glorious, but there are also many more examples of life to be found.

In conversation after conversation, I pull out these small victories, excavated from the rubble of pain. I search for them—the three tiny shells found on an empty beach. I hold them out to remind us of the promise of next year's crop, and the year after that, and the year after that. The promise of the bounty that we are growing for future generations.

Opening Thoughts
By Shira Hassan

I first started doing informal community accountability (CA) work because I was involved with a group of people who were consistently either turned away]or targeted by police and social services. I started as a young person in NYC in the 90s, when injection drug users and sex workers were establishing a harm reduction movement together. I didn't know that CA was a term. I just embraced harm reduction principles and applied them to violences of many kinds.

The first time I intervened to address harm was in the early 90s, when a friend of mine who was involved in the sex trade came to me because her boyfriend had become violent and she was afraid of what he would do. Both of them were trans people, and she did not even think about going to the police or social services. She wanted help. We established a safety plan for her, and then we confronted her abuser and said, "If you do this again to her, these three people will do the same thing to you." That was a violent solution, and I have worked in the years since to figure out more nonviolent ways of intervening.

At the Young Women's Empowerment Project (YWEP), we also couldn't access the police because we were all women of color (WOC) and trans people of color (TPOC) who had current or former experience trading sex for money. While the police were interested in surveilling us, they were not interested in helping us. Social services didn't know how to support us either. We were a non-profit, so violent ways of addressing harms were a threat to our existence. We started crafting sometimes subtle and sometimes overt strategies for interrupting and transforming violence. It was this experience that taught me that everything in CA hinges on relationships.

Once Mariame and I started talking more regularly about CA work we were doing about ten years ago, it formalized my thinking. These conversations made me appreciate that instead of a set of ad hoc strategies, what I was doing was actually a practice. I also began to realize that the messiness of CA was a normal part of this work, and that my discomfort in terms of feeling as though I was always reinventing the wheel was a feature and not a bug of doing this work.

We started Just Practice Collaborative (JPC) in 2016 as a way to transmit what we have learned in our many years of CA/Transformative Justice/HR practice. We have trained thousands of people over the years, hundreds through JPC alone. We've learned that the best way to improve as facilitators and coordinators is to JUST PRACTICE.

This workbook is hard-won knowledge, and it comes from my own experiences and the experiences of those I love--some of whom did not survive violence. It's the workbook I wish I'd had 15 years ago, and it represents the culmination of many mistakes. It's intended to be pushed back on, improved, and re-written by the next group of people who figure out how to adapt the work for their times.

We offer this workbook in the same spirit that we offer our workshops. We ask that we hold the values of:

BEING GENEROUS + GENERATIVE

This means we give ourselves permission to be students of this work and not experts. We recognize that mistakes are part of the process, and we give ourselves permission to think of conflict and struggle as resources for new ideas, better next steps, and improvements on our existing work.

TAKING CARE OF OURSELVES

We are survivors and this work is difficult. In order to give other survivors what they deserve, we must take care of our own wounds.

ANSWERING JUDGEMENT WITH CURIOSITY

It is natural to experience judgement, to put up walls, and to critique. We ask that we respond to these feelings with questions so that we can stay in solutions mode, recognize that we are all students in this together, and continue to move the work forward.

Opening Thoughts
By Mariame Kaba

I facilitated my first formal community accountability (CA) process in 2003. I was called in to support a friend who had been sexually assaulted by an acquaintance. I did not know what I was doing; and honestly, 15 years later, I still often find myself at a loss. Because every person is different, and every situation has its own patterns and unique issues, the main constant in all of these years has really been me. I've grown over the years in different ways, but ultimately, whatever CA process I facilitate, I bring myself fully to it. So do you, or so will you.

I've never been financially compensated for facilitating or coordinating any CA process. I don't even know how I would charge for one. The reason I've done and continue to do this work is because I have spent all of my adult life engaged in anti-violence work of different kinds. I want my work to contribute to eradicating violence rather than simply managing it. This is why I have a commitment to prison industrial complex (PIC) abolition as an ideology, a political vision, and a practical organizing strategy. Organizing towards an abolitionist horizon demands that we attend to harm, because harms create needs that must be addressed. I believe, as one of my touchstones, Dr. Ruth Wilson Gilmore, has written, that "Cages play no role in transformation, other than the transformation of somebody who is kind of okay, into someone who is very much not okay."

Shira and I have known each other for many years (over 18 to be exact), and we collaborated as youth workers for years before we ever seriously discussed the fact that we were both informally facilitating CA processes. It wasn't until relatively recently, during the past 8 years, that we began to talk about that aspect of our work. Before we began to intentionally discuss our CA work, I used to consistently recommend that people who wanted a good facilitator reach out to Shira, and she was doing the same on her end about me. When we finally started exchanging practice notes, we realized that we were asking many of the same questions of ourselves before taking on new processes, and that we were relying on similar practices.

Through our conversations, we recognized that we had learned hard lessons through trial and error. Both of us wished we'd had more training or preparation before embarking on facilitating CA processes. We agreed that one of the most important ingredients of an effective process was assessment of the overall situation and assessing our own capacity and skills. We realized that there was little written down about this, so one of the first things we decided to create together was an assessment tool that we believe is important for setting the stage for an effective CA process. Since then, we have written more of our hard-learned insights down on paper, and have been offering training across the country through a workshop series. Both of us, however, have other work to do beyond facilitating CA processes (which is not our primary focus).

We've committed to sharing what we've learned over the years with as many people as we can, and then moving on to our other work.

This publication is not a compilation of our workshops, and is not a curriculum or training manual for how to facilitate effective CA processes. For those looking for a terrific manual on just this topic, we highly recommend the *Creative Interventions Toolkit*. What we have created is a workbook that includes reflection questions, skill assessments, facilitation tips, helpful definitions, activities, and some of our hard-learned lessons. This workbook is specifically for people who have been or will be facilitating CA processes. It's a workbook we wish we'd had when we started doing this work years ago. It's a workbook that we plan to use in our current work. It's a workbook that is grounded in and informed by our practice and our learnings. It's not an introductory guide to community accountability and transformative justice. We're offering it as an additional resource and not as a dictate or THE LAW. Other people who facilitate CA processes would include different things in their workbooks, and we sincerely hope that they create their own and share them. We would definitely benefit from more tools and information to improve our practice.

Over the years, I've learned about CA and transformative justice not only from practicing, but also from many people and organizations. Some of these include: adrienne maree brown, Creative Interventions, Critical Resistance, Kiyomi Fujikawa, Generation FIVE, Jenna Peters Golden, Cheryl Graves, Rachel Herzing, INCITE! Women and Trans People of Color Against Violence, Mimi Kim, Erica Meiners, Mia Mingus, Philly Stands Up, Cara Page, Ann Russo, Leah Lakshmi Piepzna-Samarasinha, Ora Schub, Dean Spade, Support NY, and of course my good friend, collaborator and comrade Shira Hassan.

I offer this workbook as a way to give back some of what I've been gifted by experience and by the generosity of others. Peace.

Who is this for?

This workbook is intended for people who have facilitated or attempted to facilitate community accountability processes to address interpersonal violence. It is not a handbook for community accountability 101, nor is it appropriate for novices.

This workbook is appropriate for people who already have some counseling, hotline, or first responder experience, and who already have knowledge of intimate partner violence and sexual violence either through paid or volunteer work.

Our goal is to support other survivors of sexual and interpersonal violence who have taken on the coordination and facilitation of formal of CA processes. We want to offer a resource we both wish we could have referenced when we began this work over 15 years ago.

This workbook is intended for use as an additional resource for those who have already studied community accountability and transformative justice writings, such as *Revolution Starts at Home*, *Emergent Strategy*, *Color of Violence*, and the *Creative Interventions Toolkit*.

We hope that you take what you like or need from this offering and discard what isn't useful to you.

Don't use this if...

1. The people you want to support are in immediate crisis and danger.

2. You don't have or can't establish a team of people to support a CA process.

3. It's an active ongoing court case or if other criminal punishment authorities are currently engaged (for example, child welfare authorities).

4. You are not planning to engage participants in person to address the harm.

5. Engagement in the CA process is not voluntary. No one can be forced into an accountability process.

6. You have not read the Creative Interventions Toolkit. The CI Toolkit offers concrete, step-by-step suggestions and tools for running a Community Accountability process.

7. The assault or violence is between strangers or if you have no relationship with any of the parties.

AREA 1
Key Frameworks That Inform This Work

Our work over the years has been informed by the following frameworks, and they guide this workbook:

1. Ending Sexual Violence

2. Trauma-Informed Practice

3. Harm Reduction

4. Healing Justice

5. PIC Abolition

6. Transformative Justice

7. Community Accountability

We encourage readers of this workbook to consider the concepts that we share in this section. They are foundational to our work. It is important to note that these are concepts that we've defined for ourselves through study and practice. These are our interpretations and others will have their own. We invite you to develop your own ideas about what these concepts mean for you and your work.

1. Ending Sexual Violence

Our work has been driven by the belief that we can end sexual and gender-based violence. We believe that we can do this while ending our dependence on social services (many of which replicate prison culture) and with minimal to no use of policing.

Sexual violence occurs anytime a person is forced, coerced, and/or manipulated into unwanted sexual activity. The continuum of sexual violence includes: rape, incest, child sexual assault/abuse, ritual abuse, date and acquaintance rape, statutory rape, marital or partner rape, sexual exploitation, sexual contact, and sexual harassment.

We highly recommend that facilitators participate in training offered by your local rape crisis center to gain more specific and relevant information and to augment your knowledge. These trainings can connect you to resources and provide you with a community of people to rely on as you facilitate CA processes.

Both of us have been trained through local rape crisis centers and domestic violence agencies. We've found these workshops and trainings helpful to our practice, but there were also some gaps that we had to fill in through our own study, analysis, and practice. You should expect to challenge and be challenged by the information you hear and learn in traditional training settings. This workbook is our humble attempt to fill in some of the gaps that we encountered in traditional settings.

Victim or Survivor

There are different opinions on the use of the terms *victim* and *survivor*. Some individuals who have experienced a sexual assault refer to themselves as *victims* because they were victimized by a violent offense. This term also stresses the fact that the assault was not their fault. Other individuals who have experienced a sexual assault, however, embrace the term *survivor* because it highlights the strength required to survive sexual violence and reach out for help. The transition from victim to survivor is a personal, self-identified continuum. It is up to the individual to make their own decision. Typically, a person who was recently assaulted is referred to as a victim, while someone whose assault happened further in the past is referred to as a survivor.

It's important to acknowledge the reality that many people who experience violence don't actually survive it. In addition, disability justice challenges us to think about the survivor/victim dichotomy in more complex ways. For example, Shira lives with complex PTSD and chronic illnesses resulting from trauma. For her, the notion of survival is subjective and changes constantly.

What we mean by *survivor* is that we are still here. We will use the term *survivor* throughout this workbook.

2. Trauma-Informed Practice

Being trauma-informed is an essential element of this work; it has also become a buzzword that gets a lot of play but isn't often practiced in reality. We recommend reading and taking a training about doing trauma-informed work.

Trauma-informed work demands that you have a basic understanding of the psychological, neurological, biological, social and spiritual impacts that trauma and violence can have on people. Being trauma-informed means that we are genuine, authentic, and foster compassionate relationships with survivors.

Being trauma-informed and survivor-led means that a CA process moves at the speed of trust.

The core trauma-informed principles are:

ACKNOWLEDGMENT
Recognize that trauma is pervasive.

SAFETY
Ensure that all participants are safe in the process.

TRUST
As coordinators and facilitators, we must take trust seriously and continuously invest in building it. We can do this by explaining "what, why, and how" at each stage in the process.

CHOICE
The CA process must be voluntary and real choices about the direction of the process should be given to the survivor whenever possible.

CONTROL
As much control as possible should be in the hands of the survivor.

COMPASSION
We should only engage in facilitation if our empathy is high.

COLLABORATION
The process should be designed with input from all parties. This includes being as flexible as possible to account for how hard it is to participate in a CA process.

STRENGTHS-BASED
We should build on the existing strengths of participants rather than working from a deficit model.

How have you seen trauma play out when trying to address harm?

_____

_____

_____

_____

_____

_____

_____

_____

_____

_____

_____

_____

"In order to build the movements capable of transforming our world, we have to do our best to live with one foot in the world we have not yet created. I believe unhealed trauma is the most dangerous force on earth. It's the mechanism through which violence and cruelty and greed reproduce. Just as battered children have a higher likelihood of growing up to be battered or battering adults, oppressed people who have not had the opportunity to do the work of collective healing can end up assuming oppressor roles to others, and the pattern of feeling victimized, and believing that therefore the world owes us more than it owes other people, is particularly deadly. One response to having felt helpless in the face of horrific abuses is getting stuck in trying to prevent what's already happened. This can lead to militarization, to extreme nationalism, to the kind of opportunism that's willing to win some kind of sovereignty or security for our own group at the expense of others—which of course only continues the cycle, create new groups of desperate people." - Aurora Levins Morales

The definition below is drawn from the *Whose Security Toolkit* written by Lara Brooks and Mariame. The toolkit is greatly influenced by the work of the Young Women's Empowerment Project, Broadway Youth Center, and Project NIA.

Harm Reduction
Definition

Harm reduction is a philosophy of living, surviving, and resisting oppression and violence that centers self-determination and non-condemning access to an array of options.

Harm reduction is a set of practices that has been gifted to us by Queer and Transgender people of color, drug users, people in the sex trade and survivors of the HIV/AIDS epidemic. Harm reduction is not a public health invention or a social work intervention, even though it has been used effectively in those fields.

This framework intentionally, holistically, and creatively supports us exactly where we are, without preconceived expectations of success, while recognizing the impact of violence on our lives and communities. Harm reduction is the union of healing and community-building at its finest.

We value harm reduction practices that:

AFFIRM the expertise, self-determination, and experiences of young people.

DEEPEN our understandings of the ways in which individuals and communities experience risk, oppression, and violence—and the evolving ways we resist.

CREATE accountability through intentional and youth-led relationship building.

PROVIDE an array of options so that individuals can make informed decisions, guide their own healing processes, and practice/teach harm reduction in their own lives and communities.

Harm Reduction- what's your definition?

_____

_____

_____

_____

_____

_____

_____

_____

_____

_____

_____

_____

_____

_____

4. Healing Justice

CA processes require us to be uncomfortable and to sit with pain. How, then, can they also put us on path to healing? Ideally, community accountability can initiate a healing journey for everyone involved through an intentional process that puts power in the hands of those who were impacted by the harm. However, as those of us who are survivors know, healing from sexual and intimate violence is a lifelong process.

A CA process can take months or years, and, if done well, can create a strong foundation for ongoing healing work for all involved. This careful facilitation requires us to remember that each person is in charge of their own healing process, and that our role is to support survivors' autonomy and self-determination. The framework of Healing Justice has helped us towards our goal of facilitating a process that can put people at the beginning of their healing path without thinking of ourselves as "healers." The path from trauma to empowerment is built through reflecting the survivor's resilience and strength back to them. The Healing Justice framework reminds us that we can only be experts in our own healing--no one else's.

Healing Justice
Definition
(Taken from Young Women's Empowerment Project and the Chicago Healing Justice Learning Circle)

Healing Justice means we all deserve to heal on our terms and we confront oppressive systems that get in our way. We honor the trauma and resilience of generations that came before us and use interactive, daily practices that anyone can do.

Healing Justice is a reminder to social movements that the concept of action should be expanded to support the self-determination, interdependence, resilience & resistance of those most impacted by oppression.

Healing Justice is revolutionary in confronting the capitalist, colonial, individualistic paradigms that tell us we are alone when we seek out healing.

Our Own Healing

In order to be fully engaged in this work, it is essential that we remain connected to our own healing work and triggers. Since most of us doing this work are survivors ourselves, it is critical that we take care of ourselves, find support, and enact necessary boundaries.

Healing Justice- what's your definition?

Ask yourself the following questions to help you gauge your own needs:

1. Where are my triggers? What kinds of violence will I NOT intervene in? *(For example, harm to animals or children.)*

_____

_____

_____

2. Can I be compassionate towards someone who has caused sexual violence? Are there some kinds of sexual violence I cannot intervene in?

_____

_____

_____

3. What current support do I have in my own ongoing healing? What kind of support do I need to do the work of community accountability?

_____

_____

_____

5. Prison Industrial Complex (PIC) Abolition

In 2019, it is hard to imagine an institution more harmful than a prison. With daily reports of sexual assaults perpetrated by correctional staff, hunger strikes by those opposing long-term solitary confinement, and many deaths in custody, prisons certainly do not end violence or produce public safety. Real community safety (everyone having access to housing, food, employment, and education and experiencing freedom from violence) is not created by increasing criminalization. We need to consider transformative changes and investing resources in communities.

Both of us are PIC abolitionists. What we mean by PIC abolition is that we want to end the whole system of mutually-reinforcing relationships between surveillance, policing, the courts, and imprisonment that fuel, maintain, and expand social and economic inequity and institutional racism. So, not just prisons.

In this workbook, we rely on a definition of PIC abolition by Critical Resistance, an organization where Mariame Kaba serves as a community advisory board member.

Prison Industrial Complex (PIC) Abolition
Definition

Prison Industrial Complex (PIC) abolition is a political vision with the goal of eliminating imprisonment, policing, and surveillance, and creating lasting alternatives to punishment and imprisonment.

Abolition isn't just about getting rid of buildings full of cages. It's also about undoing the society we live in, because the PIC both feeds on and maintains oppression and inequalities through punishment, violence, and controls millions of people. Because the PIC is not an isolated system, abolition is a broad strategy. An abolitionist vision means that we must build models today that can represent how we want to live in the future. It means developing practical strategies for taking small steps that move us toward making our dreams real, and that lead us all to believe that things really could be different. It means living this vision in our daily lives. Abolition is both a practical organizing tool and a long-term goal.

What is PIC Abolition to you?
Draw/write your thoughts.

Some individuals in prison have caused great harm to people and to communities. This cannot be minimized. It's precisely why we are so passionate about the need to create community-based structures to address harm and to mediate conflicts. As survivors of violence, we want safer communities. Importantly, most people who do harm will never be jailed and/or imprisoned. As such, building community-based structures will allow us to focus on harms that our current systems of policing and punishment ignore, neglect, and/or are unable to resolve.

In 2003, Angela Davis suggested:

"Our most difficult and urgent challenge to date is that of creatively exploring new terrains of justice where the prison no longer serves as our major anchor."

As there is no blueprint/map for abolition, we must spend time imagining, strategizing, and practicing other futures. In our work, this encompasses many facets: We organize and mobilize to address the root causes of oppression and violence. We test the limits of our imagination of what is possible in terms of addressing violence and harm. We creatively re-imagine our current structures of policing and warehousing individuals. We expose the brutality and abject failure of the current system.

We foreground a revolutionary transformation of consciousness while demanding that our resources be radically reallocated. Always collective, prison abolition may/will look different from one community to the next. Yes, there are many vexing questions and unknowns to puzzle through. But we can do this together, and we believe that community accountability and transformative justice is one path to help us reach an abolitionist horizon.

"The purpose of abolition is to expose and defeat all the relationships and policies that make the United States the world's top cop, warmonger, and jailer...Abolition is a movement to end systemic violence, including the interpersonal vulnerabilities and displacements that keep the system going. In other words, the goal is to change how we interact with each other and the planet by putting people before profits, welfare before warfare, and life over death."
– Ruth Wilson Gilmore

Common Questions about Police and Prison Abolition and Responses [1]

Question	Response
What about rapists?	**Most sexual assaults happen between people who know each other--not at the hands of the stranger serial rapists portrayed on TV.** Most sexual assaults are not reported, and most people who engage in sexual assault are not in prison, so ending prisons will not flood society with predators. Further, the power given to law enforcement agents, and the situations created by imprisoning people, produce high rates of sexual assault. Policing/prison is a source of sexual assault and not a solution. Because of the high rate of sexual violence in prisons, we are essentially sentencing people to judicial rape when we incarcerate them. *Bottom line:* There are some rapists in prison, more rapists outside of prison. The prison is not a way to stop rape; the prison is the rapist.
What about murderers?	**Most people murder people they know well, often as part of complex family and relationship violence dynamics.** TV makes us think prisons are full of murderers who would go on killing sprees if released. That is an inaccurate portrayal both of how violence most commonly happens and of who is in prison right now. What we know is that the people who commit murders are actually the LEAST likely to repeat their crime.

Question	Response
What about murderers? *Continued*	They have the lowest recidivism rates. Prisons kill people through medical neglect and nutritional deprivation. Police murder people of color with impunity. ***Bottom line:*** Prisons and policing do not stop murder; the prisons and police are the murderers.
What about sociopaths?	**TV shows popularly deploy the idea of "the sociopath"—a person incapable of feeling empathy—when representing serial murderers.** Disability justice analysis can help us think critically about how medical categories are deployed to create "monsters." Do such people exist? Do some groups get targeted for such diagnoses by the white male psychiatric establishment? Does containing some small number of such people, if they exist, actually justify our gigantic, racist prison and policing system? Have such people always existed, or does our society create trauma that produces them? If so, could we get to the root causes rather than maintaining a prison system in hopes of containing them, given all the damage that system does? Today, free, high-quality mental health support is not available in the U.S., and prisons function as the largest mental health facilities in the country, yet utterly fail to deliver any effective mental health care. ***Bottom Line:*** We have to question TV portrayals of psychiatric illness and focus on building community-based support for people with disabilities rather than putting people in cages.

Question	Response

TV cop shows make it seem like prisons are full of serial killers, but prisons are instead full of people from vulnerable communities who were in desperate situations, and engaged with drugs, property crimes or conflict with their friends, lovers or family. Compare these imprisoned people to CEOs, bankers, law enforcement agencies, corporate polluters, and politicians whose actions shorten the lives of thousands or millions of people.

What about dangerous people?

Are the people in prison truly the "dangerous people"? Being in prison correlates less to dangerousness than to race, poverty, and disability.

Bottom Line: People in prisons are not the dangerous people; people running racist, anti-poor, Earth-destroying systems for profit are.

The United States has the largest prison system that has ever existed on earth, and it is a very recent invention. The contemporary world and the history of humanity are filled with nothing but alternatives to this system. It is easy to believe that any system we have lived under and been fed propaganda about is permanent and essential, but human history shows that systems of state control are constantly being invented, collapsing, and being reinvented. It is actually more unrealistic to believe that the current wildly harmful, resource-intensive, aberrant, and unpopular system of caging large numbers of humans will continue.

This is unrealistic. It won't happen.

Bottom Line: If it can be built, it can be dismantled.

Question	Response
What about public safety?	**Safety derives from healthy relationships with other people.** Prisons are focused on isolation and therefore foster violence rather than safety. People are safe when they have what they need, when they are not desperate, when they have spaces to heal from trauma, and when traumas are prevented in the first place.

Bottom Line: We do need to build safety, and we can do that through making sure people have what they need and building connective relationships and communities--not by relying on cops and cages. |

[1] Draft by Dean Spade, 2017. Many thanks to Mariame Kaba for giving feedback on this document.

6. What is Transformative Justice?

In 2007, Generation FIVE offered the following definition of Transformative Justice:

"Transformative justice (TJ) seeks to provide people who experience violence with immediate safety and long-term healing and reparations while holding people who commit violence accountable within and by their communities."

They outlined the goals of Transformative Justice as:

1. Survivor safety, healing, and agency

2. Accountability and transformation of those who abuse or cause harm

3. Community response and accountability

4. Transformation of the community and social conditions that create and perpetuate violence – systems of oppression, exploitation, domination, and state violence

Over the years, others have offered their own interpretations of TJ as a framework and approach.

For example, writer and healer Leah Lakshmi Piepzna-Samarasinha suggests that TJ is:

"any way of creating safety, justice, and healing for survivors of violence that does not rely on the state (by which I mean the prison industrial complex, the criminal legal system, foster care, children's aid, the psychiatric and disability prison industrial complex–e.g. psych hospitals, nursing homes, and extended care--Immigration, the TSA, and more)."

TJ practitioner and disability justice organizer Mia Mingus describes TJ as:

"a way to respond to violence within our communities in ways that 1) don't create more harm and violence and 2) actively work to cultivate the very things that we know will prevent violence, such as accountability, healing, trust, connection, safety." Philly Stands Up defines TJ as "a way of practicing alternative justice which acknowledges individual experiences and identities and works to actively resist the state's criminal injustice system. Transformative Justice recognizes that oppression is at the root of all forms of harm, abuse and assault. As a practice it therefore aims to address and confront those oppressions on all levels and treats this concept as an integral part to accountability and healing."

For our part, we appreciate Erica Meiners's description of transformative justice as:

"a framework [that] is often in an uncomfortable alliance with the more established and recognized practice of restorative justice."

She continues:

"As defined by the Chicago organization Community Justice for Youth Institute (n.d.), a restorative justice model is based on 'a theory of justice that emphasizes repairing the harm caused by crime and conflict.' The overall goals of RJ practices are to try to heal the whole community from an incident in which people are harmed, and ideally, to help prevent the same sort of harm from happening again. TJ, built in part through the perceived limitations of RJ, argues that the conditions that made harm imaginable and possible must be transformed, not restored, in order to build strong and just communities capable of addressing harm.

TJ questions whether harm can ever truly be healed or the victim restored, in a context where structural inequality is the pervasive norm. An inherently flexible approach, TJ is structured less as a single model, and more as a political outlook driven by values of prison-industrial complex abolition, harm reduction (the goal of reducing harm caused to an individual community by an action, regardless of whether that action can be completely stopped or prevented), and holistic healing. TJ has often taken root within organizing focusing on sexual and gendered violence. If transformative responses to sexual violence can be built, then responses to other forms of harm must be feasible."

In the words of Shira:

"The principal difference between Transformative Justice/Community Accountability and Restorative Justice is that TJ/CA must only happen outside of the state and its systems. Restorative Justice may or may not align with the state, and has no political mandate to work outside of it."

What we appreciate about TJ/CA is that these frameworks understand violence as BOTH an individual, interpersonal issue AND a social and political one. Both/and. We're not going to be able to solve our issues through social services or by working within a criminal punishment apparatus which is itself a massive purveyor of violence.

Draw what transformation feels like to you **or** think of a major transformation you've been through and chronicle it here:

I have always
believed, and I still
believe, that
whatever good or
bad fortune may
come our way we
can always give it
meaning and
transform it into
something else.

~Hermann Hesse

Transformative Justice

From Erica R. Meiners's *For the Children?: Protecting Innocence in a Carceral State* (Minneapolis and London: University of Minneapolis Press, 2016), 194-196:

I continue to participate in organizations and ad hoc mobilizations that have included a number of Chicago gatherings on engaging transformative justice, for example at DePaul University in 2009 and at the University of Illinois-Chicago in 2013. My experience with both the crisis/reactive initiatives and the wider preventive paradigm-shifting work is complex, heartbreaking, and ongoing. Two hesitant TJ processes come immediately to mind: A colleague/comrade reached out after experiencing a sexual assault and wanted a non-police intervention to hold the perpetrator accountable.

Those of us that responded to this request for a TJ process were fumbled and slow. We were effective at supporting the survivor, but less effective in figuring out how to hold the perpetrator accountable. When a student at my university was harmed by another student and initiated a TJ process, and subsequently asked to be more central to the process of building accountability for the one who had perpetrated the harm, the process veered toward shaming and collapsed. In both of these cases, an organization or an ad hoc group of people formed to try to build other responses at the request of the persons who had experienced harm.

While the outcomes were mixed, and while sharing details publicly even years later to facilitate learning is challenging, even the tentative and collective responses we formulated in each of these two incidents reframed the roles of bystanders, gathered people together to talk about collective responses, and built capacities to imagine something different. Things shifted. People moved. [...]

Much of this work is also ad hoc, undertaken by everyday people on their blocks, and is not archived or documented. Several years ago, my household decided that we would no longer be silent witnesses to an ongoing "domestic disturbance." For two summers, we watched the police roll up to the house two doors south of our building to respond to verbal and sometimes physical altercations between a heterosexual couple with alcohol and drug problems. Like everyone else on the block, we sat in our backyard and ignored their fights. No one wanted to get involved. It was a private matter. They are always high or drunk, and clearly crazy. Hell, we might have gotten hurt ourselves. After enough yelling, someone on the block might finally call the police, and one or both people might be picked up, but they would return days later.

After deciding to not look away, my household strategized and formulated a loose plan that was neither radical nor labor-intensive. We introduced ourselves to this couple who lived two doors south and made a point to have repeated conversations about mundane topics in moments when no one appeared in crisis or high or drunk. We talked about the weather, food, life. We found out that one of them had chronic debilitating health problems. We talked to other neighbors about what was going on and about how to reduce the police presence, which no one in the neighborhood wanted. We moved from hanging out in the backyard to also sitting on our front stoop and talking to the people that walked by.

When we heard yelling and what might be violence, at least two of us walked over and said, "Hi. Is everyone okay?" Our actions changed the neighborhood in small ways. People on the block talked to one another more. We shared information about other issues on our block: elderly neighbors that needed help, annoying dog owners that did not pick up dog poop, bad landlords. One of the two individuals moved away for a spell, and on their return it was quieter. The police visits were reduced to a trickle.

Perhaps the violence was driven inside, into the basement or behind locked doors and windows. Perhaps our friendliness was interpreted as social shaming. Perhaps we simply masked the problem. Yet this experience did give us a new way of thinking about our block, about the work of community, the relationships between neighbors, and the idea that a bystander is never neutral but rather plays an integral role.

6. What is Community Accountability?

In their modern iteration, as developed and framed by groups like INCITE! Women and Trans People of Color Against Violence, community accountability practices and processes are partly about mapping possibilities for transformation and healing. They can be an important component of transformative justice (TJ). The people who helped to found INCITE! came to their understandings of CA through lived experiences with pushing for more laws to combat gender-based violence and/or with being targets of the criminal punishment system. We recognized that the CJ system increased violence in our lives. We looked for alternative systems for addressing the interpersonal and systemic harms that we were experiencing in our communities. Community accountability and transformative justice practices emerged from the lived realities of women of color, trans people of color, and others who were navigating violence.

In 2010, several people met in Miami for a National Gathering on Transformative and Community Accountability, convened by the Audre Lorde Project and other groups. The participants created a collective definition for CA that has been useful for us:

Community Accountability
Definition
(The Audre Lorde Project, National Gathering on Transformative and Community Accountability, 9/2010)

Community accountability (CA) strategies aim at preventing, intervening in, responding to, and healing from violence through strengthening relationships and communities, emphasizing mutual responsibility for addressing the conditions that allow violence to take place, and holding people accountable for violence and harm. This includes a wide range of creative strategies for addressing violence as part of organizing efforts in communities when you can't or don't want to access state systems for safety.

In 2012, INCITE! defined CA as "a process in which a community--a group of friends, a family, a church, a workplace, an apartment complex, a neighborhood, etc.--works together to do the following things:

1. Create and affirm values and practices that resist abuse and oppression and encourage safety, support, and accountability

2. Develop sustainable strategies to address community members' abusive behavior, creating a process for them to account for their actions and transform their behavior

3. Commit to ongoing development of all members of the community, and the community itself, to transform the political conditions that reinforce oppression and violence

4. Provide safety & support to community members who are violently targeted that respects their self-determination

Bad things can and do happen. Some people inflict suffering and pain on others. How can we effectively intervene to address these harms? This is the question that animates community accountability processes and practices.

Our promise to each other is not that we can always prevent harm. What we can do is be present to help each other get on a road towards healing when harms inevitably occur. We can accompany each other through the pain and suffering. At its most basic, community accountability (CA) is about keeping one another company and intervening when harm happens. It isn't a program and it isn't new. It isn't inherently transformative or restorative; in fact, some CA practices are punitive.

What is Community Accountability?
Draw/write your own answer.

Community Accountability

Writer Nate Marshall shared a recollection about growing up in Chicago and getting beaten up by a group of teenagers in his neighborhood. The incident illustrates one form of community accountability:

When I was in eighth grade I was attacked. Two of my friends and I were waiting for the bus when we were approached by a group of six kids from high school. This crew attempted to intimidate us into giving them money. Once it was clear that we wouldn't be so easily shook, they jumped us. A few seconds into the assault two of the guys stopped and called off their friends. They recognized me from the basketball courts in our hood. They said I was cool, and the other guys relented. They did, though, try to jump my other two friends (who weren't from our hood). After about a minute of small fight between the three of us and the six of them, a car slowed down and called out and the crew of six ran.

Later that evening my mom called the police, and they came to our house. They told us nothing could be done. Even though I knew two of the guys by face and nickname, they said basically everyone in our neighborhood, myself included, fit their description.

After they left, my mom called my oldest sister and told her what happened. She reached out to some of her friends who were high-ranking gang members in our hood and told them. They knew me as a smart, studious kid who went to magnet school and was a decent pickup basketball player. By the end of the week every member of the crew that jumped us had come to my house and rung the doorbell to offer an apology. The gang members offered me a restoration that the police were unwilling or unable to offer.

Source: Page May and Nate Marshall, "Toward the Unreasonable," in *The End Of Chiraq: A Literary Mixtape* (2018)

Nate's story underscores the fact that, for many people, the police aren't helpful. In some neighborhoods, cops in fact exacerbate conflict; in others, they don't bother to intervene at all. As such, people have had to figure out for themselves how to intervene when harms happen.

As already mentioned, we can't ensure that human beings won't hurt or harm each other. That's impossible. We can, however, work on how we respond to harms and hurts when they occur in our communities. CA is not about minimizing harm, making excuses, or helping people who cause harm to avoid consequences for their behavior and actions. If a process is doing these things, then it is not actually accountable to victims/survivors and our communities.

As we consider various forms of harm, it's important to remember that our goals should be first and foremost to address survivors' immediate needs. Often this doesn't involve engaging in a protracted community accountability process. Sometimes survivors can quickly and clearly identify their needs, and in other instances it takes time for people to know what they need.

Community accountability and transformative justice approaches treat violence as a problem rooted in systems of oppression, rather than one primarily based in individual conflicts. TJ teaches us to insist on accountability over punishment, whether it's for a child who pushes his teacher in a classroom or for someone who kills another human being.

Important Considerations About Community Accountability

CA processes should be **voluntary.**

There are four key values/characteristics that are foundational to all CA processes:

TRUTH
Radical honesty with yourself and others.

TIME
Expect everything to take longer than you anticipate.

TRUST
An imperative to assume best intentions. This even applies to the person who has caused harm unless/until they have shown a lack of integrity in the process.

TRANSFORMATION
A change in behavior and a commitment to avoid harming in the same way again.

Three important questions guide CA processes for us (gleaned from restorative frameworks):

1. Who has been hurt/harmed? *(Centering those who were harmed.)*

2. What do they need? *(Justice is defined as meeting the needs of multiple parties, including victim/survivor, PWCH, and community, with the goal of more healing and maybe transformation.)*

3. Whose obligation is it to meet those needs? *(Bringing a broader group into the process of accountability.)*

Ten Guiding Questions For Any Community Accountability Process

1. We want people to recognize their mistakes and commit to improving. How do we achieve this goal?

2. Where is the harm and where is the potential healing?

3. Distinguish between abuse and conflict. Is the harmed party unsafe or uncomfortable?

4. Determine if this is abuse or conflict and identify who was victimized. What is the originating action? Is the harm a response to that action?

5. What does the survivor need right now?

6. How can I/we make this better?

7. What change are you hoping for? Do you actually want this person to learn and do better, or just to feel bad about what they did? It is important to be honest with ourselves about the answers to these questions.

8. How does this address and/or transform the root causes of violence?

9. Who has the power? How might they use it?

10. **Evaluation:** Have we actually made things better for the harmed parties?

Is the Community Accountability Process Appropriate?

Over the years, we have used these questions to help us decide if we can/should take on a community accountability process. It is helpful to get answers to most of these questions before offering to play a role in a process, especially a coordinating role.

Guiding Questions

1. What happened?	Get both the facts and the multiple truths of the situation.
2. Who is impacted? How?	Assess whether you have relationships with any of the people impacted and also what the scope of the process might be.
3. What do the impacted parties want?	Try to understand whether the demands are realistic and whether the goals are achievable.
4. What do the impacted parties need from the facilitators and/or the process?	Align the demands with what might be expected from you and others.

Guiding Questions Continued

5. What are the short/intermediate/long-term steps for delivering on wants and needs?	Begin to map out some of the steps in this process.
6. How much time will this take?	Assess your capacity to see the process through to completion.
7. Think about the timing of the process.	Acting too soon could cause more harm if you haven't gathered enough information or if the survivor is not ready. Acting too late can also cause additional harm.
8. How will we communicate?	Begin to determine, and to create a plan around communicating with, the audience for this process. There is always an audience, even if it is not articulated at first.
9. What available resources exist? Which resources must be developed?	Who can help support you and the process?

Guiding Questions Continued

10. *Am I the best person to facilitate this process?*	Assess whether you're the right fit. *(See self-assessment questions in Area 2.)*
11. *Who can I enlist to join my team?*	Map out a potential team.
12. *Does this conflict actually need an accountability process? Can the issues be resolved without a process?*	Not every situation requires a community accountability process.
13. *Will a community accountability process actually move things forward? Is there a reason to think that a process could make a positive impact?*	This is important because there are times when conflict or harm has gone on for so long that a process will not help.

Guiding Questions Continued

14. Has either party participated in a community accountability process before? If so, what happened? Was it for the same issue? If so, why would a process work this time if it has not before?

Consider whether the parties involved are likely to fully engage in the process and/or be responsive to any resulting consequences.

15. What are the power dynamics at play?

There are certain dynamics for which a community accountability process will not work—for example, an executive director and staff member or pimps and police, just to name a few.

16. Is there a plan for dealing with backlash?

There is often some backlash following a community accountability process.

17. How will we plan for sustainability?

Is there a plan for folks to rotate responsibilities and have backup people who can move up if someone needs to tap out?

Guiding Questions Continued

18. How will we document practice?

Not all processes can be documented. Mariame always documents in her private journals. Shira does not do documentation at all. What is your practice and why it is important?

19. How will we celebrate?

Many times some kind of honoring and closure is needed that brings joy. It's important to ask the survivor how and if they would like this included in the process.

Thanks to Leah Lakshmi Piepzna-Samarasinha, brilliant writer and thinker on transformative justice, for her suggestion of questions 17-19.

Summary

To be an effective CA process facilitator, four habits of mind are helpful. These are your superpowers. With them, you can move through the challenges of facilitating processes.

TRY SHIT

Effective facilitators are always experimenting and testing new approaches. Failure is a given, but it can be an opportunity to practice creativity. Keep trying until you find what works for you and your practice.

IT'S A PROCESS

This means it will take time to move through and that it is likely to be messy. You may make progress one day and feel like you've hit a wall the next. Don't be afraid to change course whenever you feel it's warranted.

ASK FOR HELP

You are a facilitator, not a lone ranger. Good facilitators know that they are not alone and that it takes a TEAM to make a good process work. Collaboration is KEY.

FAILURE IS A GIVEN

CA/TJ practices "interrupt traditional and linear notions of progress and success and failure" (Meiners, 2016). Cultural studies critic Judith (Jack) Halberstam (2011) reminds us that "Under certain circumstances, failing, losing, forgetting, unmaking, undoing, unbecoming, not knowing may in fact offer more creative, more cooperative, more surprising ways of being in the world." Thinking, organizing, and acting beyond the success/failure binary whenever possible is instructive. Messiness in a process is the norm rather than a "failure." Get comfortable with this.

Note About CA Processes, Labor, and Money...

We have never charged money for facilitating a community accountability process for a number of reasons.

First...
We recognize that all parties who choose to participate in CA processes are laboring. We're all giving of our time, sharing knowledge, and co-creating the process. We don't believe that facilitating processes is about expertise but rather about democratic participation toward pre-figuring the world in which we want to live.

Second...
These processes can be years long and any costs would be beyond what anyone could reasonably afford to pay. We aren't interested in commodifying relationships, the critical part of any process.

Third...
It's highly unlikely to conduct a process without mistakes and the exchange of money often means someone is viewed as a provider of a service or as an expert in some way. CA processes are not about service provision or expertise.

Lastly...
The professionalization and commodification of community accountability is counter to our personal values. We do this work because it's our political commitment to our people and because we are committed to working towards an abolitionist horizon.

Recognizing that facilitating CA processes is gendered work adds another layer of concern to any discussion of labor and money. Most of the people who are facilitating CA processes focused on interpersonal harm identify as women and gender nonconforming people. Often the people who have caused interpersonal harm identify as men. Under patriarchy, women and gender nonconforming people's labor is exploited. We understand why people want to be paid for their labor and time. For us, however, we've decided to operate in line with our overarching values and to try to live those in the present. We don't judge others who decide to operate according to theirs.

AREA 2
Food For Thought

There are a number of issues that present themselves when you take on the facilitation of a community accountability process. In the following pages, we offer our thinking and ideas based on our own practice and experiences. We've tried to provide some answers to the questions that have plagued us in our own work and those that we are often asked by others.

Once again, it's important to know that these are our answers and that other practitioners (including you) will have your own. We offer these ideas with humility, fully cognizant of the fact that there are no experts in facilitating CA processes. We are all always learning, making mistakes, and trying to improve.

In our training and workshops, we often share the following essay by Bench Ansfield and Jenna Peters-Golden, titled "How We Learned Not to Succeed in Transformative Justice."

We have found it to be foundational to our practice of community accountability. So we offer it to you and include some space for you to reflect on it as you embark on your facilitation work.

"How We Learned Not to Succeed in Transformative Justice"
by Bench Ansfield and Jenna Peters-Golden, in Make/Shift Magazine: Feminisms in Motion, Issue 12, 2012.

A person is called out by their ex-partner for sexual assault and intimate-partner abuse. She is a committed prison abolitionist who believes in gender justice and transformative justice. And she wants to clear her name. The co-director of an immigrant-rights organization is asked by his colleagues to leave his position, and refrain from organizing around immigrant justice, until he can demonstrate that he has identified and unraveled the patterns of abuse that led to his sexual assault of two interns. Members of a collective house search for ways to hold an undocumented, transgender housemate accountable for crossing sexual boundaries without banishing her from their community, thereby making her vulnerable to harassment, imprisonment, and deportation.

These are just a few examples of the types of people and organizations who have requested a facilitated community-accountability process from Philly Stands Up (PSU), a volunteer collective that has been doing transformative-justice work for nearly a decade.

For those just learning about transformative justice and community accountability, it is often surprising to hear that many of the people we have worked with over the past eight years have come to us on their own. Many who have perpetrated assault agree to work with us out of a political devotion to finding ways to address harm without calling upon cops, courts, and prisons. This political unity—along with the fact that we share community with most of the people we work with—gives us leverage to facilitate a process of transformation that does not rely upon punishment or shaming.

Frequently, an even greater factor than political unity in pulling someone into an accountability process is their desire to clear their name. Whether or not they enter the process believing they have done anything abusive or violent, most people we work with believe that upon completing a process they will attain a stamp of approval from PSU. They want to be considered a success.

And they are not the only ones wanting to declare transformative justice a success. Among the most common questions we are asked when introducing our work is, "What is the success rate of your accountability processes?" More often than not, this question is asked in search of hope and reassurance that transformative justice can offer an effective intervention into the prison industrial complex. And although generating faith in alternatives to the criminal-legal system is a critical function to transformative-justice organizations, we feel there is no easy answer to this question.

Our hesitation does not stem from a lack of belief in the possibilities of transformative justice, but from ambivalence about the concept of "success." Success is conventionally understood as signifying completion and resolution, as opposed to reflecting the jumble of small victories, uncertainties, and defeats that typify organizing work.

There is no such thing as a "successful" accountability process on those terms. At the very least, we hope to mitigate the impact of the harm that has occurred, and prevent it from happening again. This harm-reduction model may be accompanied by breakthroughs and triumphs—such as fulfilling a demand list laid out by a survivor or unpacking the patterns of behavior underlying the violence—but even these moments do not register successes.

Success presumes that there is a way to undo the harm that has occurred, to come out of an accountability process with an unqualified victory. But in an accountability process, it is critical to remember that there is no way to undo harm, that each moment of progress is paired with moments of failure or dismay, and that healing is not the same as curing.

If we reach for "success," we are undermining the work. Instead, Philly Stands Up strives to celebrate triumphs without forgetting to scrutinize and learn from mistakes.

We have developed this analysis out of necessity.

In one of our accountability processes, when a person who had perpetrated assault started making headway—demonstrating her capacity to communicate hard emotions, nurture self-empathy work on her ableism and transphobia, and de-escalate potentially violent situations—we got caught up in the thrill of participating in her transformation and lost sight of our roles as facilitators. Instead of appreciating her progress and staying on track with the work she had yet to do, we started to feel invested in her success.

Once we became focused on "success," we tended to pay less attention to the patterns of abusive behavior that this person still needed to work through, focusing instead on the strides she had made. We found ourselves approaching the work in ways that we associate with the nonprofit industrial complex: looking for easy, marketable victories with the goal of generating statistics, and glossing over contradictions and inconsistencies that might call our work into question.

With our PSU peers, we were able to identify how the success model had snuck into our facilitation, made us vulnerable to burnout, and compromised the process. We rebounded by casting aside our fixation on breakthrough victories, and remembering to celebrate small gains.

We committed ourselves to documenting the more subtle advances made in a process. It is easy to ignore them, focusing instead on the tremendous amount of work that remains to be done. Transformative justice thrives when a balance can be found between those two poles, and we have found that documentation is key in striking this balance. By taking note of moments that may seem of little consequence—such as punctual arrival to a meeting or direct eye contact—we can draw a more accurate and nuanced map of how a transformative process evolves. Changes in behavior, after all, happen slowly. Without documentation, they can go unnoticed.

This tactic should not be mistaken as "patting perpetrators on the back" for not hurting other people (a practice we don't use), because it is always paired with a commitment to documenting the areas that still require work and attention, even when we thought the process had evolved beyond them. accountability processes are not linear: they do not involve moving a person who has perpetrated harm from point A to point B on a straight line. Entailing frequent roundabouts, U-turns, and abrupt stops, they must be adaptable and strong. Where a success model might seek to push through the disappointments, convolutions, and complexities intrinsic to this work, our approach aspires to hold a transformative process in its messy entirety.

And that includes how we are allowing the work to impact us affectively. How should this work feel? A success model involves adrenaline, dramatic victories, and prioritizing momentum over process. But movement work is full of disappointments, hiccups, and small wins. The task is not so much to achieve breathtaking victories, but rather to make our organizing so nourishing and resilient that we can weather mistakes, build off of failures, and appreciate the revolutionary potential of even the subtlest gains.

Question

What are, in your opinion, the **3 main ideas or takeaways** of this essay?

1. _____

_____

_____

2. _____

_____

_____

3. _____

_____

_____

In our opinion, the 3 main ideas or takeaways of this essay are:

1. Processes are ALWAYS messy, so it's important to move past thinking about the success/failure binary. Instead, let's consider trying/improving as our frame.

2. Accountability processes are not linear.

3. There is no way to undo harm through an accountability process. Harm causes wounds. The wounds heal but never disappear.

Section A:
Assessing Yourself, Your Capacity, and Your Skills

1. Self-Assessment

The most effective facilitators have the ability to accurately assess their skills, capacity and talents. Self-awareness and self-reflection are key.

Before you agree to facilitate a process, ask yourself:

1. What traits and skills do you possess that you think will make you an effective CA process facilitator?

2. Do you have any experience holding or mediating conflict in a paid or unpaid role?

3. How do you handle conflict in your own life? Do you avoid it? Do you rush towards it?

4. Are you a good listener? How do you know?

5. What is your capacity for empathy? *(See Empathy Quotient Questionnaire below.)*

6. Do you work well with others? Are you a lone ranger?

7. How angry are you at the person who caused harm?

8. Are you in close relationship with any of the parties involved?

9. How do you plan to care for yourself throughout this process? Do you have an individual support system away from this conflict that can hold you down?

10. What are your emotional triggers?

11. What is your block? What kinds of conflict resolution/mediation do you know you would NOT take on, either because they are too triggering or because you are not ready? *(For example, harm done to children, abuse of animals, or whatever your personal bottom line is.)*

12. What is your capacity for this work? Be honest. These are long-term processes; they require hours of sustained work and almost always take more than 6 months to complete.

13. Do others ever ask you to intervene in and/or mediate conflicts?

14. Have you ever been involved in a public takedown? Did you initiate it, or were you the subject of the public callout? What did you learn from it?

10 minutes

Do you have criteria or questions for deciding to participate in an accountability process as a coordinator or a member of survivor/PWCH teams? What are they? What do you ask yourself?

_____

_____

_____

_____

_____

_____

_____

_____

_____

_____

_____

_____

_____

2. Skills and Characteristics of Effective CA Facilitation

Here are some traits that are useful for CA facilitators to strive toward. None of us embodies all of these characteristics, but if you keep them in mind as you move into your facilitator role, they will serve you in the process.

- Good listener
- Reflective
- Present
- Trusting
- Supportive
- Encouraging
- Nonjudgmental

- Respectful
- Fair
- Aware
- Inclusive
- Open
- Brave
- Humble

- Able to keep things moving
- Able to appreciate humor
- Organized
- Open to other opinions
- Collaborative
- Honest
- Patient

- An anchor
- Disciplined
- Willing to forgive
- Approachable
- Flexible
- Holistic
- Able to create safe space

5
minutes

What do you think are the key skills and characteristics needed to effectively coordinate and/or participate in CA processes? Why? Draw/write your thoughts.

Empathy: A Critical Resource in CA Facilitation

Arthur P. Ciaramicoli (2000) defines empathy as "the capacity to understand and respond to the unique experiences of another person." It is "feeling with people."

Dr. Ciaramicoli (2016) writes that:

"Empathy is frequently confused with sympathy, but the two are different. Sympathy is the capacity to identify with another person's experience even when we do not actually know whether our experiences are similar. For example, sympathy is at work when you hear of a neighbor's father passing away and immediately respond, 'She must be devastated! I certainly was when my father died.' A few days later, though, you might hear that your neighbor's father left the family when she was a baby, and seldom had any contact with his daughter. In fact, she was not devastated at all by his death. Where sympathy rushes in, empathy takes time to understand the facts. Sympathy, which is often driven by immediate emotion without considering the facts of a situation, can cause more harm than good. Generalizations are the last thing people want to hear when they long to be understood."

Empathy guides us in the accurate understanding of situations and relationships. Empathy is also the key to negotiating and resolving conflict. Since empathy is not a tool or a technique that can be mastered, but rather an innate capacity, it requires careful nurturing and constant attention. CA offers meaningful contact with an empathetic, understanding person. Such relationships enable us to resolve our hurts and can help inform us on how to move on. We really cannot resolve our hurts alone. Without input from others, we repeat our thought patterns and can continue to cause harm.

With empathy as a guide, we learn to read others better.

Watch: Brené Brown, *Empathy vs. Sympathy*
https://www.youtube.com/watch?v=1Evwgu369Jw

Make: Empathy zines
https://cloudchamber.cc/for/mcn2018/DIYempathiZINE.pdf

Practice: Empathy Quotient Questionnaire from *The Stress Solution.* *We recognize that both the terms "empathy" and "listening" have ableist roots. In a CA process, it is important to assess your capacity to make people feel understood. We offer these tools as a potential resource for you to measure your readiness to engage in a process. These tools work well for some facilitators and may not be helpful for others.*

What is empathy? Why is it important in CA processes?
Write your thoughts.

_____

_____

_____

_____

_____

_____

_____

_____

_____

_____

_____

_____

_____

"With empathy, we're with the other person's feelings. That doesn't mean we feel their feelings. We're just with them while they are feeling those feelings. Now, if I take my mind away from them for one second, I may notice I have strong feelings of my own. If so, I don't try to push my feelings down. My feelings are telling me I'm not with the other person, that I'm home again. So I say to myself, "Go back to them." Marshall Rosenberg, *Living Nonviolent Communication* (2012), p. 69.

Empathy Quotient Questionnaire

Read the following statements and, as honestly as possible, assess whether each is true for you. For those that are, record that statement's number.

1. I have been told by more than one person that I lack empathy.
2. I have been told by more than one person that I am empathetic.
3. I feel good when I help another person.
4. I don't feel much when I help another person.
5. I feel obligated to do the right thing.
6. I enjoy giving of my time to others.
7. I am uncomfortable when people talk about emotional issues.
8. I am not uncomfortable when people talk about emotional issues.
9. I don't know what it means to express empathy.
10. I understand what it means to express empathy.
11. I often feel that I miss emotional cues.
12. I pick up emotional cues easily.
13. I have been told that I need to be right.
14. I don't place much value on the need to be right.
15. I seldom talk beyond the surface with friends.
16. My friends and I have deep conversations.
17. I prefer to not be around young children.
18. I love being around young children.
19. I think I tend to take more than I give.
20. I think I tend to give more than I take.
21. I find it easier to show animals affection rather than people.
22. I can give affection to animals and people equally.
23. I have often been called stubborn.
24. I am often told that I am easy to get along with.
25. I prefer to talk more than listen.
26. I prefer to listen more than talk.
27. In most of my conversations I talk more than I listen.
28. In most of my conversations I listen more than I talk.
29. I am uncomfortable getting close to people.
30. I feel comfortable being close to people.

Scoring

+1 point
Statements: 2, 3, 6, 8, 10, 12, 14, 16, 18, 20, 22, 24, 26, 28, and 30

-1 point
Statements: 1, 4, 5, 7, 9, 11, 13, 15, 17, 19, 21, 23, 25, 27, and 29

Results
13-15 points: High empathy

My statement numbers	My final score

3. Listening

All of us have a fundamental need to be listened to and to be understood. Listening empathetically creates a feeling of trust, which releases the "compassion hormone" oxytocin, reducing fear and bias and creating a feeling of safety. These brain changes promote open communication, giving us access to conditioned emotional learning and enabling us to restructure distorted thinking and reduce stress.

Listening well helps community accountability processes in several ways:

1. The coordinators and facilitators understand the situation and the important issues.

2. An atmosphere of respect for each person's right to express feelings and opinions sets a relaxed but serious tone.

3. Coordinators and facilitators can model attentive listening for the participants.

4. Coordinators and facilitators develop alongside the parties involved in the process.

Question: Are you a good listener?

Question: How do you know?

The purpose of listening is to understand. This is different from agreeing with the speaker.

Listening well means:

ATTENTION
You notice both the emotion and the content conveyed by the speaker. You are not thinking about what to say next.

WITHOLDING JUDGEMENT
While you are listening, you put aside thoughts of what the person "should" or "must" do, who is right, or what you would have done in that situation.

OPENNESS
Your face and posture show that you are listening. You look at the speaker, if you can, as well as others present to see how each person is reacting.

CARING
You are aware of the speaker as a person and are interested in his, her, or their concerns.

Listening Exercises

1. Listen to one person

Listen to someone without comments, questions, or opinions, until the person moves on to another topic. Do not explain what you are doing beforehand. If asked, say "just listening."

2. Listen to a group

In a group setting, try for about 20 minutes to listen as well as you can. Keep a piece of paper at hand to jot down times when your mind wandered, when you made silent judgements, when you wanted to interrupt. What kind of talk was easiest to listen to?

3. Observe a group

In a group situation, tally the number of times you hear anyone interrupting.

You might also count the number of times:

• One person finishes another's sentence
• Someone abruptly changes the subject
• Someone offers unsolicited advice
• The words "should," "ought," "must," or "have to" are spoken
• Two or more people are talking at once

It could also be interesting to observe how age affects conversation. Are children interrupted more? Do older people tend to give advice or orders more than younger people? What differences do you see between conversational roles of people across gender, race, and other differences?

4. Take silent time

Promise yourself ahead of time that you will not talk at all--say, from noon to 3 p.m. on a certain day. Concentrate on listening and observing what happens around you.

Notice:

• What was difficult about not communicating easily and quickly?
• What was it like to take the role of observer?
• What kinds of nonverbal signals did you use? Which did you notice in others?
• How did people react to you? What does this tell you about the function and politics of communication? Of listening attentively?
• How did silence help communication?

Cheat Sheet of Tips

1. **Listen.** Don't make up what you are going to say in response while others are speaking. Devote 100% of your attention to listening clearly without judgement or reactivity.

2. Be direct. No running on endlessly or wandering about.

3. Stay on the subject. Don't avoid.

4. Don't drag up the past. Stick with now.

5. Don't assign blame. Problem-solve.

6. Don't try to win. Make your objective to gain understanding and find workable solutions.

7. Make "I" statements (I feel…, I am…, etc.), rather than "third party" statements such as "you…," "one…," and "they…" .

8. Don't assume. Ask.

9. Don't speak for others, and especially don't tell them how they feel.

10. Don't make threats. You can state consequences. Know the difference.

"Facilitate" simply means "to make easier." Facilitators concentrate on participants' common task.

Facilitators provide:

CONFIDENCE
Giving the group energy and momentum, i.e. "You can do this!"

DIRECTION
Choosing productive approaches to the group's tasks; helping to set ground rules; keeping things on track; handling disruption.

TONE
Creating an atmosphere which encourages respectful, nonjudgmental attitudes, and helping participants deal with difficult, discouraging moments.

OVERVIEW
Helping the group look at each part of the problem; at each point of view; at the past, present, and future.

SENSE OF PROGRESS
Reminding the group of what they have already accomplished; building morale; contradicting "we're getting nowhere" feelings.

Facilitation Skills Used in CA Processes

Attending

Paying attention means:

• Listening
• Understanding both feelings and content of message
• Being comfortable with silence
• Noticing verbal and nonverbal cues

Modeling
The facilitator's behavior and attitudes set unspoken standards for the group.

Responding
Responses check understanding, help people clarify their thinking, and define the topic of discussion.

Specific skills include:

- Paraphrasing
- Summarizing
- Acknowledging emotions
- Outlining
- Clarifying
- Withholding one's own opinions

Getting information
Effective use of questions can help bring out needed information and can help the group decide how to use that information.

Helpful questions:

- Draw out necessary information
- Help the speaker focus
- Clarify areas of confusion
- Encourage the speaker
- Provide safety to speak
- Gently challenge the speaker to think about other perspectives and possibilities

But they do not:

- Put the speaker on the spot or make her/him/them feel tested
- Cross-examine the speaker
- Moralize or use loaded language
- Answer the question for the speaker
- Suggest what the answer "should" be
- Probe irrelevant subjects

Often, the most helpful questions are **open-ended**, giving the speaker plenty of freedom in how to reply: "What happened, and how did you feel about it?" or "What else bothers you?"

More **directive questions** can help focus on specifics: "What could you do to improve x, y, z?"

Sometimes **narrowly-focused questions** are helpful to clarify vague areas or provide reality checks: "Are you willing to accept x, y, z?"

To be avoided are questions that imply a preferred answer: "Would you agree that honesty is important?

An important skill is knowing when additional information is not needed.

Keeping silent

This skill is a test for outgoing people and for those who like to be helpful! Resisting the urge to offer advice, opinion, sympathy, or moral judgement is not easy. It is necessary, though, if the participants are to be empowered to work out their own solutions.

Concreteness

A facilitator must often bring discussion back to specifics. This means asking people to speak for themselves; breaking topics into bite-size chunks; translating general remarks into description so that "He's a pain" becomes "He calls me twice a day," or "We need to be more considerate" becomes "I need my desk to be for my own use only."

Setting boundaries and shepherding

This skill involves keeping the discussion within agreed-upon or useful guidelines. A facilitator also tries to prevent emotions from escalating beyond control.

Balancing power

When one side is weaker, more timid, less able to speak fluently, or outnumbered, the facilitator helps balance negotiating power to make sure that all parties have a fair say, and that all perspectives are considered.

Watching group needs

The group might need a break, a bit of light humor, an encouraging word, or a change of pace. Check that everyone can see and hear the rest of the group.

Problem-solving

The facilitator walks the group through problem-solving steps when they cannot direct themselves.

This means providing a structure for participants to:

- Identify issues
- Set priorities — which matters must be solved now? Which matters can wait?
- Choose an easy problem to start with
- Bring out a variety of suggestions
- Select a suggestion or combination of suggestions
- Decide how to carry out the solution
- Test for true agreement

The facilitator must also maintain a broad view of the problem, seeing different possibilities, anticipating various roadblocks, and helping the group think seriously about alternatives and consequences.

Confronting problem behavior

"Confronting" simply means clearly naming the problem and insisting that it be corrected. It need not be rude or overbearing, but it does need to be firm.

Refer to the following guidelines for when, how, and where to confront conflict as a facilitator.

When	When any behavior consistently stalls the group's progress, e.g., name calling, interrupting, scapegoating, nastiness, stonewalling, lack of good faith.
How	"What I see happening here is…" "If you keep interrupting, we cannot continue."
Where	In front of the group or in private. Be sensitive to people's need not to lose face.

Section B:
Vexing and Consistent Issues in CA Processes

1. Punishment vs. Consequences

People often come to us as facilitators seeking justice or revenge. Part of our job as facilitators is to help identify which consequences are realistic and can be actually be achieved. It's also critical as facilitators to listen through the anger and the pain on all sides. Revenge should never be the desired outcome of a process.

The United States has an addiction to punishment, which is evidenced by our overflowing prisons and by our consistent warmaking. That's the cultural context within which we are all operating when we seek alternative ways to address harm. People often come to us wanting a more accessible and effective version of a court, because there is a strong societal belief ingrained in us that court is tantamount to justice.

There is also a belief that an accountability process is the "easy way out" or "soft," and that punishment is "tough" and "true justice." As discussed in the accountability section of this workbook, punishment is passive--it happens to someone. It does not require taking responsibility or transformation. Accountability is actually harder because it requires real transformation--accountability is active.

The idea of punishment is that those who have done bad things deserve to suffer for their actions and/or behavior. Punishment is rooted in the notion that human beings are evil and sinful creatures who need to repent and be punished.

We have spent many years thinking about how we can condemn harm and seek accountability while also caring for the person who caused harm. This is important to us because we will never ever "bring to justice," through the legal system, every person who does harm in our society. It is impossible. We also believe that relying on the criminal punishment system to provide "justice" or repair harm is futile and violent.

We cannot, under any system, "prosecute" every person who causes harm. Yet many survivors and victims become consumed with seeking "accountability" through a system that simply cannot provide it. This is understandable as it is typically the only option that is offered. People deserve accountability for harms they experience. We do not believe, however, that punishment constitutes accountability. We do not believe that relying on a violent system to end violence makes sense.

As facilitators, there have been a number of times when we've both talked through wanting to kill the person who caused harm.

The thing that has been more helpful is thinking through the meaning and definition of these four words:

1. **Punishment:** suffering, pain, or loss that serves as retribution. Penalty or fee for wrongdoing.

2. **Consequences:** the results or effects of an action or condition.

3. **Accountability:** willingness to accept responsibility for one's harmful actions or behaviors.

4. **Justice:** recognition of harm done; restitution; having resources to begin our healing path; putting in place resources to prevent more harm in the future.

Before you begin a process, take some time to **write down what these words mean to you** in a given situation. This can be a useful guide to help interpret where other people's needs fall in relationship to your own.

Punishment: _____

_____

_____

Consequences: _____

_____

_____

Accountability: _____

_____

_____

Justice: _____

_____

_____

A Helpful Resource...

Chart

The chart below has been instrumental in shaping our thinking about the differences between punishment and consequences. This chart, based on restorative justice, describes how we traditionally address violence versus how we could address it in more transformative ways.

It was developed by: Paul McCold and Ted Wachtel in 2003 | https://www.researchgate.net/publication/237314664_In_Pursuit_of_Paradigm_A_Theory_of_Restorative_Justice

We've made minor adaptations to the chart for our own use.

Upper-left Quadrant

The upper-left quadrant describes how we currently engage with harm by being punitive and offering low levels of support. Examples: mandatory school suspensions; zero tolerance policies; the criminal punishment system.

Bottom-left Quadrant

The bottom-left quadrant suggests how we can sometimes address harm by ignoring or neglecting it. We pretend that it didn't or isn't happening. Examples: Letting it go when one child hits another because we are too tired to intervene; letting a privileged person with power off the hook because we think we cannot stop them or we are numb to their behavior; knowing that a friend has engaged in bad behavior and choosing not to say anything.

Bottom-right Quadrant

The bottom-right quadrant describes an orientation to harm that allows it to continue by making excuses for the person who caused harm (PWCH) and by not expecting them to take responsibility for their actions. Sometimes we attempt do the work of repair and making amends on their behalf. Other times, we invoke the very real impact of oppression as a reason to permit the PWCH not to take accountability for their behavior. Example: Someone who is multiply marginalized based on identity is not asked to be accountable because of their social location, lack of resources, etc.

Top-right Quadrant

The top-right quadrant illustrates what it means to engage in restorative or transformative justice. In this situation, we do not minimize harm, and we work with people to encourage them to take accountability for what they've done. Example: A successful community accountability process.

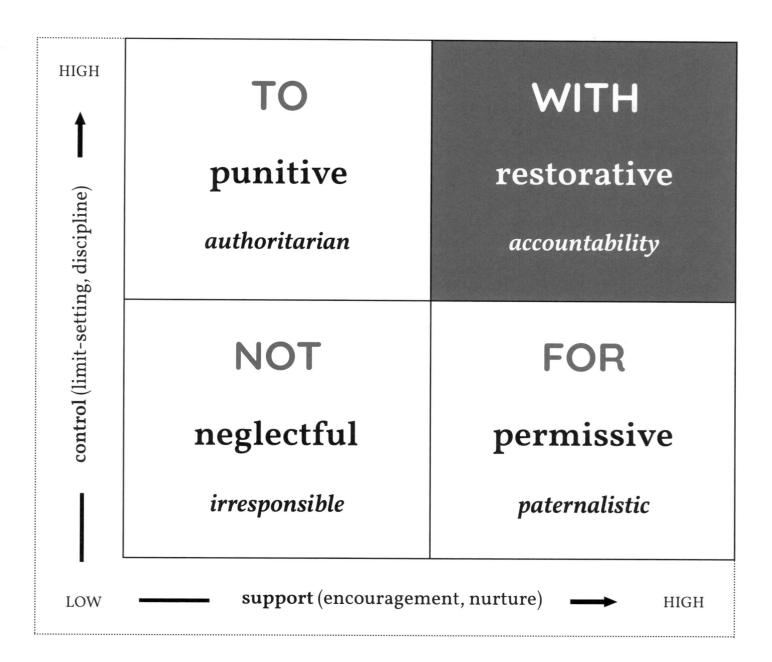

Take a moment to reflect on this chart, and ask yourself when you have responded in ways that fit within each quadrant.

How will you challenge yourself to reach for the top-right quadrant?

_____

_____

_____

_____

_____

_____

_____

_____

_____

_____

More thoughts about punishment vs. consequences

When we're operating through a punishment lens, our focus is to inflict cruelty and suffering...

We ask ourselves:

• What suffering does this person deserve?
• How can this person pay (hurt) for what they did?

When we're operating through an RJ/CA/TJ lens, our focus is on the transformation of behaviors and on the motivations for behaviors...

We ask ourselves:

• What impact/effect has this behavior had? On whom?
• What are the immediate needs as a result of this behavior?
• What can we do to address these needs?

A kindergarten teacher who is a friend and has attended many of the Just Practice Collaborative workshops gave us this helpful list of questions she asks herself when trying to assess an appropriate consequence for harm:

When trying to assess an appropriate consequence for harm:

1. Does this consequence feel like a natural consequence for the harm that happened? Am I trying to create a spectacle with this consequence?

2. Does this feel more like revenge? Am I going down the eye-for-an-eye route, or am I trying to stop immediate harm and offer support for healing and growth to happen?

3. Am I getting vindictive pleasure from this consequence instead of finding a way to make amends?

4. Are we figuring out what both the person who was harmed and the person who has caused harmed need in order to heal? Or are we trying to replicate the same pain and humiliation that happened when the initial harm took place?

5. Consequences are not universal. Asking a person who has caused harm in one setting to leave could be a consequence for one situation and a punishment in another. Always return to the thought: what outcome do we want with this consequence? An end to immediate harm and a path to healing, or revenge and reciprocal pain for the person who caused harm?

6. When you recognize that you have put into place a punishment masked as a consequence, you have the opportunity to stop, make amends for the hurt that you may have caused, and start over. Don't leave the situation because you messed up! Apologize, make amends, and move forward.

7. Check in with people who are removed from the situation to assess if they can understand how you arrived at a certain consequence. I constantly am sending messages to my best friend asking, "Does this sound right to you? Was that harsh or does this make sense?" Reach out to someone who is not afraid to call you on your shit! Messing up doesn't make you a bad person; just be honest with yourself and stay true to your goal of moving forward with harm reduction, healing, and reconciliation. This shit is hard, and it's impossible to not make mistakes.

The role of consequences:

• Consequences can promote safe spaces and create opportunities for transformation.

• Consequences occur naturally, sometimes unanimously, based on the cultural norms or expectations of the community.

• Consequences are the reaction to what's happened, and can include dialogue, reality-testing, and a commitment to unlearning sexism, cis- sexism, misogyny and violence.

2. Disposability/Boundaries

There is a critical principle in our work which states that "No one is disposable." This is because so much of our community has been separated and marginalized through ongoing targeting by the state. It is essential that our CA practices do not replicate the state and the criminal punishment system.

This does not mean that people should not have boundaries. Survivors may rightfully choose to never see or engage with the person who harmed them ever again. It is even possible to conduct a CA process without the survivor ever having to see the person who harmed them. It is also possible for you as the facilitator to decide to not have contact with the PWCH after the process concludes.

The assumption behind removal as punishment is that fear of the punishment will deter future harmful behavior in the PWCH and others. However, the assumption behind removal as a consequence of harmful behavior is that the removal will increase safety for the survivor and the community (where lack of safety was a result or effect of the harmful behavior).

Boundaries are a healthy and essential part of the healing and recovery process. Boundaries may also be a natural part of the consequences or outcomes of a CA process.

Here are some examples to help you distinguish the difference between consequences and punishment:

Boundaries or Natural Consequences	Disposability Culture
Loss of relationship between the survivor and the person who harmed them	Requiring the person move out of town
Loss of relationship between the PWCH and people who love/care about the survivor	Shunning

Boundaries or Natural Consequences	Disposability Culture
If the PWCH's work is directly related to the harm caused, it is fair to ask that the PWCH find a new way to make a living *(for example, if you lead workshops on sexual violence and are called in to a process for rape)*	Never allowing that person to make a living again by informing all future employers or by internet doxxing.
Asking the PWCH to move out of living spaces shared with the survivor or people who love/care for the survivor	Pursuing landlords or housing collectives and demanding this person not be rented to
Asking the PWCH to step back from mutual spaces either for a period of time set by the survivor or until the end of a CA process	Requiring the person to permanently remove themselves from all community activities/spaces

Remember: removing someone from a position of power is not the same as disposing of them.

As Dean Spade (2018) has written:

"We live in a society based on disposability. If we want to build a different way of being together, we have to look closely at the feelings and behaviors that generate the desire to throw people away. Humility, compassion for ourselves, and compassion for others are antidotes to disposability culture. We all make mistakes and have a great deal to learn from each other."

3. Survivor-Centeredness

As coordinators and facilitators, we are often also survivors. Being intimately involved in a process can contribute to our own healing, and can be a trigger for our own pain.

When a survivor is healing in a way that angers us, how will we respond? When a survivor wants something we also want but can't achieve, what will we do?

Solidarity with survivors is always the priority in a CA process, and has always been our priority in the processes we've facilitated. We need to continue to grow and deepen what survivor-centeredness means in the CA process, because the way we think about it is often deeply influenced by, if not wholly downloaded from, the criminal punishment system.

So much in the criminal punishment system and in mainstream anti-violence activism creates a "perpetrator vs. survivor" duality. This binary is essential to the criminal punishment system and is dependent on the idea of survivors as "innocent" and "perfect." However, this emphasis on the "innocence" of survivors places us on a pedestal, erases our humanity and complexity, and pressures us to be compliant.

This polarization has left us with a belief that someone can't be both a survivor and perpetrator. This can mean that we become reluctant to engage the other party because we're not able to hold complexity. This presents a challenge in CA/TJ work because our goal is to transform all involved in the harm, whenever this is possible.

At its best, community accountability removes the idea of what survivors are "supposed to be" and "supposed to want," and gives us an honest opportunity to be in anger without enacting revenge; to experience healing without erasing the harm we experienced. It allows us to be in a transformative process with our own healing, without that process belonging to the state or our therapists. It frees us from prescriptions about the "right way" to heal. It allows our voices to be the true center of the process.

In order to reclaim the idea of survivor-centeredness, survivors can work to identify their needs and wants alongside the persons who committed harm.

Survivors of harm have complex needs. They can't/won't all be met by a CA process. It is important to know and understand this from the start to help you set realistic goals.

As we consider various forms of harm, it's important to remember that our goals should be first and foremost to address survivors' immediate needs. Often, this doesn't involve engaging in a protracted community accountability process. Harms engender various needs. Sometimes survivors can quickly and clearly identify these. Sometimes it takes time for people to know what they need. We discuss the idea of wants and needs later in this workbook.

Some considerations to keep in mind:

1. People who were harmed in one relationship or context are capable of being harmful in previous or later relationships.

2. Find some questions about who is most harmed in the violent situation in the *Creative Interventions Toolkit* (Section 2, page 24).

3. The cycle of violence can be further enhanced by the criminal punishment system.

4. Most people who are causing harm have experienced either institutional or family violence; this means that everyone in a process can have a claim to survivorhood. For a CA process to be effective, two people have to be valued, which immediately sets off alarms. It creates a challenge because we have to keep processes survivor-centered. We need to have two people seen in the process and valued. We need to look at the person who caused harm in the most complex way so that transformation can happen. This makes us uncomfortable.

What does survivor-centeredness mean to you? What does it mean in your work? How will you prioritize it in your facilitation/coordination? How will you honor this principle when it's being challenged?

_____

_____

_____

_____

_____

_____

_____

_____

_____

_____

_____

_____

_____

4. Wants/Needs

"I do not believe our wants have made all our lies holy." – Audre Lorde (Between Ourselves)

When facilitating community accountability processes, we spend a lot of time working with people to express their needs and wants. These will determine the goals of the process, so they are a key component for ensuring effectiveness. Needs are resources that life requires in order to sustain itself. Wants are our desires: things that we might like to have but aren't essential to our survival.

All of us as human beings are trying to get our basic needs met. Fulfilling our needs is the motivation for our actions.

Below are some needs--things we must have in order to stay alive--that we all have:

- Physical needs – food, clothing, shelter, safety, water
- Social needs – belonging and affection
- Individual needs – knowledge and self-expression

Our needs are often unconscious, and we develop strategies to meet needs that we have not even consciously thought of. One of the most important things to ascertain in CA processes are the needs behind the statements made by survivors and people who cause harm (PWCH). Identifying these motivating needs is necessary to constructively and effectively solve problems.

Your job as a facilitator is to help each party identify what they need and want from the process. Mariame uses the following guideposts to help people who have experienced and/or caused harm to distinguish needs from wants and desires.

What do victims of harm say they need?
[according to Ruth Morris]

1. Answers

2. Recognition of their wrong

3. Safety

4. Restitution/repair

5. To find significance or meaning from their tragedy

Mariame usually adds another category to this list, which is "prevention." Many survivors who she's worked with over the years want to at least try to make sure that the same actions don't happen to another person. Another common need is "connectedness and belonging."

Survivors' understandings of justice are nuanced and complex. Some social scientists have used the term "kaleidoscopic justice" to explain how some survivors of sexual harm and domestic violence discuss their needs and wants.

Kaleidoscopic Justice
Definition
(McGlynn and Westmarland, 2018)

Kaleidoscopic justice is justice as a continually shifting pattern, constantly refracted through new circumstances and understandings. The variety of patterning resonates with victim-survivors' sense that justice is not linear, but has multiple beginnings and possible endings. Justice is complex, nuanced and a difficult to (pre)determine feeling. Justice is a lived, ongoing and ever-evolving experience and process, rather than an ending or result. Within this pluralistic conception of justice, a number of key justice themes, elements of the kaleidoscope, emerged: namely consequences, recognition, voice, dignity, prevention and connectedness.

Once we've identified needs, we ask: "What can be done to meet these needs?"

Next, create a list of wants. Wants will always be negotiable in a process, while we will do our best to meet needs. Make sure it is made clear to people that needs will become the guideposts for the process. We have to stick to them and not deviate. Wants often shift. Needs must remain constant throughout the process.

Sometimes survivors don't know what they need or want. That's OK and normal. As a facilitator, you can help support people as they identify their needs and wants. You can offer suggestions and you can allow everyone time to think about what they need and want.

Resource: https://journals.sagepub.com/doi/full/10.1177/0964663918761200

5. Magic Words

We've both found ourselves constantly searching for the "right words" as we facilitate CA processes. Some words open up people's hearts and others can shut them down.

Some helpful words we've found to open up dialogue include:

- Would you be willing to…?
- What do you need?
- What else is true?
- What would it look like if?
- What would it take for this to feel doable?
- What are you willing to do?

6. Accountability — A Breakdown

[SECTION 4F of CI Toolkit has a comprehensive focus on taking accountability, including worksheets, etc. We highly recommend that you read and study it]

The word "accountability" is thrown around liberally, but is very poorly understood. There is no way to "hold people accountable." People can only "take accountability." Accountability is a continuous, active, and voluntary process of being responsible to yourself and those around you for your choices and the consequences of your choices. Unlike punishment, it is something that we do rather than something that is done to us.

Connie Burk of the Northwest Network in Seattle, Washington, defines accountability as "an internal resource for recognizing and redressing the harms we have caused to ourselves and others," rather than as "something that happens to bad people."[i]

Taking accountability means that we expect consequences for actions that we take, that we take responsibility for harms that we have done, that we understand the impact(s) of those harms, and, finally, that we focus on repairing them.

TJ practitioner and disability justice organizer Mia Mingus explains:

"True accountability is not only apologizing, understanding the impact your actions have caused on yourself and others, making amends or reparations to the harmed parties; but most importantly, true accountability is changing your behavior so that the harm, violence, abuse does not happen again."

The clearest way to assess accountability in a process is to do a statement of impact with the PWCH at the beginning of a process. This statement does not need to be public or shared with the survivor; it is simply to document the understanding that the PWCH has about the harm they have caused. Doing this at the beginning of the process creates a baseline that can be used to track changes in understanding of the behavior and the motivations that caused the harm. There is an excellent tool to use for this in the CI Toolkit (Section 4A, page 26).

Sometimes when we speak to people about the value and promise of community accountability and transformative justice, we are confronted with the question, "What if the person causing harm doesn't want to accept responsibility for his/her actions?"

And the truth is that there is no good answer, except to say that in our current culture, resisting accountability is normal. Our struggle is to figure out how we are going to develop structures in our communities to encourage people to be accountable for the harm that they cause others. We want to focus less on individuals and more on our role in fostering a culture that makes abusers believe that it is acceptable to harm another person. People who cause harm are not islands unto themselves. They don't exist in a vacuum. Often they are people we love and have lifelong relationships with.

So each of us has a stake in figuring out how we are going to build a system that truly addresses harm and helps people to take accountability. If we make sure to keep survivors and marginalized populations at the center of our analysis, there is a good chance that the new system that we build will be better than the one we currently have.

Useful resource on accountability: Building Accountable Communities Videos | http://bcrw.barnard.edu/event/building-accountable-communities/

"Accountability is the corollary to grief for those of us who are responsible for harm. I shared the ways in which I have witnessed accountability as an unparalleled tool for transforming shame for our responsible parties in Common Justice. I wrote about the way I have become persuaded that accountability does for those of us who commit harm what the healing process does for us when we are harmed: it gives us a way to recuperate our sense of dignity, of self-worth, of connectedness, and of hope—the things we lost when we caused harm. In this work, I have come to see accountability as something that is as essential as a grieving process to restoring us to our best selves." Danielle Sered, *Until We Reckon*.

A Useful Reading...

The following excerpt from a blog post by Mia Mingus resonates with our experiences of facilitating CA processes and offers lots of food for thought. We share it here and invite you to consider your thoughts about accountability.

Mia Mingus
https://batjc.wordpress.com/2018/01/04/new-year-intentions-and-practicing-accountability/

Being accountable to others and ourselves is something we must learn how to do well, just like anything else. These are hard skills that require the discipline of practice, commitment and faith, knowing that we will make mistakes and fall short many times—most times. This is especially true in a society steeped in punishment, privilege and criminalization; that actively avoids accountability and does not encourage the kind of culture, relationships or skills needed to support true accountability. For many of us in years past, I am sure we have made resolutions or set new intentions, only to find them broken or given-up on within months, weeks, or sometimes days. This is very common, and many of us carry familiar shame and guilt every year about it. It is important to remember that resisting accountability is a natural part of accountability. It doesn't mean we are bad people, it means we are human. In our TJ work, I always encourage people to stop treating resisting accountability as something to be outraged or thrown-off-guard by, but instead to understand it and plan for it, knowing that all of us have resisted accountability at some point in our life and will again. Get a plan in place for when you will inevitably resist accountability. Practicing this in small

ways can help us down the line when the stakes are much higher.

A good reminder is to get support from those you trust around your accountability. For example, if you are trying to start a new daily practice, set-up an accountability buddy that you text every day—even if your text is "I didn't do my practice today." Or connect with others who are working on similar goals. Or find someone that you can check in with consistently who will be able to support you and with whom you can have nuanced conversations about your accountability. Note: it is not their job to "hold you accountable;" that is your job.

One thing we know from our work is that accountability happens in relationship. Attempting to transform deep-seated behaviors, habits, and beliefs is incredibly hard to do alone; and even smaller, seemingly benign behaviors often have deeper roots. Accountability is often bound up with healing and tackling our trauma is work best done with someone(s) we trust and can rely on. For example: if you are trying to prioritize your self care, you will at some point have to confront why you have been neglecting your self care for so long. You will have to feel into why you have not been valuing yourself or how you put other people's needs in front of your own. After all, if it were as simple as just scheduling time in your calendar, it would have already been done.

Supporting someone else in their new year's resolution or intention is also a great opportunity for learning. Often when we are in TJ processes, we have an accountability team, a group of people who are supporting the person who caused harm to take accountability. This is a different kind of skill set that is critical for us to practice. Supporting someone in their accountability is hard work, and anyone who has ever tried to do it knows what I am talking about. Learning how to support someone in their accountability without minimizing the harm they've done, or demonizing them, is much easier said than done. Again, we can practice these skills now, which can help us prepare for later. Similar to fire drills, we can practice when there is little-to-no-threat, so that when there is a fire, we are not starting from zero.

The following section is an excerpt of writing by Danica Bornstein and Shannon Perez-Darby when they were at the Northwest Network of LGBT Survivors of Abuse. We so appreciate being able to share this information with readers.

Self-accountability is a process we do with ourselves, for ourselves. When we are being accountable to ourselves, we are acting in a way that honors ourselves and our values. We are acting with consciousness and integrity by taking responsibility for who we are in the world and for living in alignment with our values.

Self-accountability is the basis for being accountable in all of our relationships. However, accountability does not require other people to be in the process with you. You can take accountability for things you have done or harm you have caused whether or not the person(s) impacted by that harm are able or willing to engage with you. In "The Secret Joy of Accountability: Self-accountability as a building block for change," Shannon Perez-Darby defines self-accountability as "a process of taking responsibility for your choices and the consequences of those choices. [...] In a process of self-accountability, this reconciliation isn't dependent on another person's involvement, but instead engages with our own sense of values and what is important to us. In the work of self-accountability, we are constantly striving to align our actions and our values, knowing it's likely they will never be exactly the same. When there's a gap in that alignment we can reflect on what choices we would need to make in the future, so our actions are more in line with who we want to be.

Proactive self-accountability involves:

1. Checking in with yourself when making choices.

2. Becoming aware of the values you have in any given situation.

3. Being honest with yourself about how you feel and what you want.

4. Asking yourself why you made the choices that you did in the past. *(What was going on for you at the time?)*

5. Thinking about what you need in order to make choices in the future, or in order to change your behavior so that your actions are more in line with your values.

Accountability in Relationships

How do we create a process of accountability when something comes up in our relationships?

The process will look very different depending on the situation and the people involved, but there are some consistent elements that seem essential to every process:

• **Being present and truly hearing the consequences and impacts of our actions.** Often when we feel bad about what we've done, we're all the more anxious to rush to the resolution stage, bypassing the part when we really think about and hear the impact of what we've done. This helps explain why some hurts seem to get resolved while others seem to hang around forever.

• **Really understanding what happened, locating our "6" and owning it.** *[Read the "Secret Joy of Accountability" to learn about locating your "6"].*

• **Making a plan that addresses the consequences, and a plan for the future.** Such a plan can involve many things; for instance, simply deciding to knock it off or just apologizing, or repairing the harm we've caused. If we believe our behavior was not good and didn't match our values, we should develop a plan to not do it anymore, even if we can't accomplish this overnight.

The process of accountability requires agency, which is a sense of yourself as a person who can act powerfully and make choices on your own behalf. In developing a plan for accountability, it is important not to take the approach that once you've hurt other people, you have to do whatever they say until they feel better. Agency is about maintaining equity in relationships. Each person's agency is essential to creating accountability in relationship to one another.

Resources:

"The Secret Joy of Accountability" | https://drive.google.com/file/d/0Bw8WCsF3KC3AcGtNeGcw-WGs3QVk/view

"How to Fuck Up" | http://portlytruestories.blogspot.com/2007/11/how-to-fuck-up.html

Building Accountable Communities | http://bcrw.barnard.edu/building-accountable-communities/

Taking accountability does not necessarily require participation in a CA process. There are many ways to hold yourself accountable without involving the survivor (although these can also occur in tandem with a CA process).

Practices/Processes For Self-Accountability

1. Removing yourself from social situations in which you have abused your power in the past. For instance, if you are a musician who used shows to meet people you've violated, not playing shows until you've done some monitored growth in this area—fans look up to performers, and there is a real power imbalance in this relationship.

2. Being transparent about your process.

3. Asking close friends if they will hold you accountable on a day-to-day basis, check in with you to see if you're doing the work, and/or check you if you do or say something fucked up.

4. Not expecting your taking accountability to solve the harm you've done in the past. Trust can only be repaired if both parties agree that it can. All you can do is go forward in the future and try not to cause more harm.

5. Not asking for plaudits from the public for doing this work, and not accepting speaking engagements or money for talking about how you learned not to become an abuser.

The above section was adapted from: Jes Skolnik | https://medium.com/@modernistwitch/on-accountability-d79957d1a17d

7. Conflict Resolution and Mediation

We do not consider ourselves to be experts at conflict resolution. In fact, Mariame has never taken any conflict resolution courses or participated in specific training. Conflicts do arise in CA processes and they do need to be addressed. However, CA processes are not rooted in conflict resolution. CA processes are also not the same as mediation.

Mediation allows disputing parties to explain what has happened. Mediators do not try to determine what "really" occurred, who is telling the truth or who is at fault. The focus of a mediation session is on the future: what will happen from now on? This orientation lends itself to disputes between people in ongoing relationships: friends, family, neighbors, co-workers, community groups. Sometimes disputes between people in more limited relationships, such as landlords and tenants or consumers and small businesses, are also addressed. Mediators who work with environmental disputes, divorce, or other specialty arenas have advanced training in those areas.

We recommend that CA facilitators seek out mediation training if available in your community.

When conflicts have arisen as part of a CA process, Mariame has used the following tool for the parties involved as a way to discuss the conflict. It's a document adapted from a guide developed by the Plum Village Lineage North American Dharma Teachers Sangha.

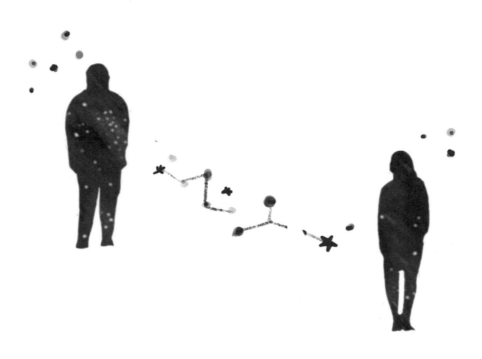

Interpersonal Conflict Analysis Form

....

1. Describe the conflict, in chronological order, to the best of your current ability and objectivity. It is often difficult to separate description from interpretation, yet that is what is being asked of you here. *Attach an additional page if needed, but please be brief and to the point. If it is hard to be succinct, you may need more reflection time.*

_____

_____

_____

_____

2. Which of my personal beliefs and values are at play in this situation? For example, how was conflict handled in my family of origin? How has my experience within my family and other formative environments influenced my usual reaction to conflict (e.g., fight, flee, or freeze)? How might the past be shaping my perceptions and experience within this conflict? *(You may wish to address this on an additional page.)*

_____

_____

_____

3. How am I a part of the situation?

_____

_____

4. Who else is involved in the difficulty?

_____

_____

5. How and when and by whom were the other people involved informed that we perceived a difficulty between us?

_____

_____

6. How am I contributing to the problem?

_____

_____

7. What have I done to try to resolve the conflict?

_____

_____

8. How have others tried to help resolve this situation?

_____

_____

9. What outcome do I want personally?

_____

_____

10. **What outcome do I want for my broader community** *(if applicable)*?

_____

_____

11. **In what ways am I (or could I be) keeping things stuck/unresolved?**

_____

_____

12. **What is my power (formal and informal) in this situation?**

_____

_____

13. **In what ways could I promote movement and resolution?**

_____

_____

14. **Please consider which of the following seem to be going on and then consider how they inform my current understanding of the conflict.**

Power conflicts	Personality conflicts	Information problems
Hidden agendas	Value conflicts	Erratic personal behavior
Inadequate policies/processes	Territorial/boundary conflicts	
Cultural differences	Organizational structure	

Communication problems:

☐ Lack of   ☐ Rumors/gossip

☐ Inaccuracy of   ☐ Other *(describe briefly)* _____

15. In my view, do additional community members need to be included in order to reach a resolution? If so, who are they, how do they need to be involved, and how do I suggest accomplishing this?

_____

_____

_____

16. What elements or conditions does a solution need to include or meet? (What does "resolved" look like?)

_____

_____

_____

17. What are the alternatives to resolution?

_____

_____

18. What ways do I see that this conflict could be resolved right now?

_____

_____

19. In the absence of a solution agreed between the parties, am I willing to agree to abide by a decision made by CA facilitator acceptable to each side?

☐ Yes   ☐ No

Attach additional pages as necessary to completely respond to any questions for which space is inadequate. But remember that brief, succinct, to-the-point answers probably will serve you and the process best.

8. Public Apologies — A Template

Apologies, sincere ones, are underrated. True apologies are acts of courage and humility because they put the person who is offering the apology at risk. The person who apologizes must do so without knowing whether it will be accepted. In our society, they also risk being "punished" if they acknowledge that they have done something wrong or caused harm.

Over the past couple of years, we've noticed an uptick in attempts to publicly acknowledge harms. These attempts have mostly landed badly. Frankly, this is sometimes because the public statements have been unhelpful or have compounded harms. AND sometimes it's because the apology is directed at a generalized public instead of the person(s) who were actually harmed. AND sometimes it's because people don't actually want to allow for the possibility that people are truly remorseful and want to change. AND sometimes it's because people don't actually want accountability; they want revenge and punishment. It is important to be discerning about the full spectrum of apologies and responses.

As people who have been facilitating and continue to facilitate community accountability processes, here's what we would like to offer to people who have caused harm. If you are going to make a public statement (which is not warranted for every type of harm), it should be short and it does NOT have to be self-flagellating.

Our humble suggestion for a good and sufficient public acknowledgement of harm includes the following language:

"I caused harm. I'm sorry."

Acknowledge that you've harmed people and say you are sorry. You do not need to write a dissertation listing everything you've done for public consumption. It is not the world's business.

"I have apologized to the person(s) I've harmed."

Always try to apologize directly to the harmed parties first. They are the ones injured, so they are your audience. If you are asking for forgiveness, it must be on their terms. More often than not, the person you harmed won't even ask you for a public statement.

"I am educating myself so that I never do the same thing to anyone else."

Demonstrate that you are taking accountability and concrete action to change.

"I'm working on myself to gain understanding of my actions and to ensure I don't repeat the harm."

People who we hurt often want us to do our best not to repeat the same harm again.

"I will devote/commit myself to trying to repair the harm I caused."

If your public acknowledgement of harm is more than 8 sentences, cut it down. Also, please remember that you are doing this to take accountability for what you've done and not because you expect to be patted on the back. Finally, KEEP IT MOVING (stay off social media), and do the difficult work needed to begin a transformation of the harm. Review the *CI Toolkit* for details on writing harm statements.

The advice offered in this section is focused specifically on public apologies. If you are writing a personal or private apology, you might include more information.

Resources:
- http://www.sorrywatch.com
- http://www.sorrywatch.com/2013/06/11/how-to-apologize-a-short-checklist/

9. Forgiveness

Survivors don't have to forgive. That's not what we mean by transformative justice. If they want to, they can, but they are not required to do so. The onus is on the person responsible for the harm to take accountability. You should remind all parties of this truth regularly.

There's a lot of messaging in society that suggests that you can't heal unless you forgive, or that transformation and restoration are tied to forgiveness.

This is victim-blaming and can cause additional harm. A demand for forgiveness can shift attention to the person who caused harm to the detriment of the person who was harmed. Pay attention to whether this is happening in a process.

Sometimes we have found that survivors are interested in forgiving themselves for how the harm has impacted their lives, their relationships, etc. A process can be a good space to explore this.

Activity for Self-Forgiveness

1. Establish the situation requiring forgiveness. Select one if there are several. *(What did I do? To whom, when, and how? You may want to write this down.)*

2. Work to understand your own situation which led to this action. *(Why might I have done this? What was going on with me?)*

3. Specify clearly what expectations you had of yourself that you did not meet. *(What I expected from me was... What I did was...)*

4. Do you wish to stop punishing yourself and feeling bad for what you did? If yes, proceed.

5. Imagine the person(s) you harmed, including yourself. Alternatively, place a picture(s) on a chair in the room with you.

Say aloud: "I deeply regret that I [name the harm]. Yet it serves no purpose for me to continue to punish myself for this action. I deeply regret the harm that you suffered. Wherever I can, without causing further harm, I will make amends to you. I now will release my self-recrimination, self-criticism and unhelpful guilt. I choose to let it go and be free of it."

"Forgiving and being reconciled to our enemies or our loved ones are not about pretending that things are other than they are. It is not about patting one another on the back and turning a blind eye to the wrong. True reconciliation exposes the awfulness, the abuse, the hurt, the truth. It could even sometimes make things worse. It is a risky undertaking but in the end it is worthwhile, because in the end only an honest confrontation with reality can bring real healing. Superficial reconciliation can bring only superficial healing."-- Desmond Tutu

10. Repeat Harm-Doers

This is an area where we've both felt challenged. We have witnessed people who've gone through processes be called in for second and third processes for the same behavior.

Sometimes this is because the first process wasn't effective; sometimes the process was fine, but the person is not making satisfactory changes. So, how do you decide when to do a second or third process with someone? And if you don't do a process, what do you do instead?

In our own practice, we've facilitated a second process with the same person before but never a third.

> **Critical questions to ask before engaging multiple times with the same person include:**
>
> 1. What would be different about this process than the previous one(s)?
>
> 2. What has the person learned since the first process?
>
> 3. What have you learned since the first process?
>
> 4. What is your capacity to actually hold another process?

We don't have any easy answers for how to handle a community member who repeatedly engages in the same type of harm. Sometimes an intervention can be made outside of a formal process, such as telling that person that they need to step back from certain positions of power or roles. Other times, a community might seek the removal of the person who is causing this harm from particular spaces. We need to collectively think through more ways to create safety for ourselves and our communities.

11. Relationship-Building

Relationships are foundational to community accountability processes. This is a multi-layered reality.

You must be in some type of a relationship with the people who are central to the community accountability process. Unless you have been working on community accountability in your hometown for a significant amount of time, and you are trusted and well known, being connected to a third party is usually not enough of a relationship to hold a process together.

This is because the CA process relies so much on the facilitator/coordinator being respected, trusted, and in charge. Given how fraught and upsetting CA processes are, if you do not start with a base-level relationship, it can be very difficult, if not impossible, to keep a process on track when it inevitably becomes wobbly.

It can also be dangerous to attempt a process if the people involved do not know each other well or do not know you well. For example: in cases of stranger rape, community accountability processes may not work because there is no way to effectively call that person in and no way to assess the level of ongoing danger to you or the survivor.

12. The "Truth" — Dealing with the Desire for Vindication or Establishing Fault

We've both found ourselves constantly searching for the "right words" as we facilitate CA processes. Some words open up people's hearts and others can shut them down.

Some helpful words we've found to open up dialogue include:

• **Repeat the following:** "Even if everyone agreed on what happened, what happens from now on is most important to our process right now."

• Acknowledge the desire for revenge, but be clear that effective CA processes cannot be about this.

• Lying — remind people that we are assuming all participants want to engage in the process in an honest way.

• As Shira often says in trainings, multiple truths can co-exist, and people's truths can change as their understanding or memory of what happened evolves.

• Just because the survivor's story changes doesn't mean they are lying — trauma causes us to remember events in fragments, and our mind often protects us from having access to the whole memory.

• We've both found ourselves constantly searching for the "right words" as we facilitate CA processes. Some words open up people's hearts and others can shut them down.

13. How to Get People to Engage in a Process

Persuading people who caused harm (PWCH) to participate in a CA process can be difficult; some don't understand what a process is, others are skeptical that a process will yield positive results, and still others are resistant to taking accountability or are in denial about the impact of the harm they caused. They may be reluctant to address harm or conflict, or they may feel too angry, too discouraged, etc.

We've heard many excuses from PWCH who aren't interested in engaging in a CA process. Everyone in a CA process must be there voluntarily, and it's best if they join with a willing and open attitude. Openness can also be accompanied by feelings of doubt, fear, or elements of denial. Part of the CA process is engaging with these common dynamics.

As a facilitator or coordinator, you walk a fine line between encouraging participation and pressuring people to do something they may not be ready or willing to do.

The following are some ways that you can invite people to participate:

1. Give information. After explaining what will happen in a process and why it can be beneficial, you can mention that they decide whether or how to participate, and can always step away if they are not satisfied.

2. Give people time to think things over.

3. Ask them what they might want to see happen if they did participate in a process. Can these goals be achieved in a different way?

4. In careful and non-threatening manner, remind the PWCH that what they did could invite the involvement of the criminal punishment system.

This section only addresses the PWCH, NOT the survivors.

Survivors should never be compelled to participate; many times the survivor remains anonymous, and a process can still continue without their involvement.

14. Backlash — Preparing for and Expecting It

Backlash is inevitable in many processes. The backlash frequently comes from third parties who have strong opinions one way or another but don't have critical information. People sometimes want to deal with backlash by sharing confidential information or by being very transparent. That instinct, while good, can be counterproductive, since the people who are actually involved in the process deserve privacy. **This means that you, as the facilitator/coordinator, will be the primary target of backlash because you are unable to divulge the details of the process.**

Questions regarding backlash:

1. Where is the backlash coming from?

2. Do you need to respond to it? Why?

3. Will responding to it cause additional harms? Will responding preclude healing or will it enhance it?

4. Is the backlash critically important to the success of the process?

5. What information is the backlash providing about the process and whether it can be improved?

If backlash is coming from within your team or from participants, then it may mean that the process can no longer continue, or that you are unable to serve as facilitator/coordinator.

Examples of this that we have heard or witnessed:

1. Facilitators or coordinators being put on blast (via gossip or social media) by people involved in the process.

2. The process being reported to criminal legal authorities, either by a process participant or a third party.

3. The survivor or PWCH being targeted for participating in the process either on social media or through other means, like getting people fired or evicted.

15. Recipe for Guaranteed Ineffectiveness

- Don't set any goals for your process

- Don't do a self-assessment

- Be a lone ranger instead of building a team

- Fail to differentiate between punishment and consequences

- Mirror the adversarial criminal punishment system in your process

16. How to Know When a Process is Over

How to know when it's over if it went well:

• Have you achieved most of your goals?

• Is everyone in basic agreement that the process has come to a close?

• Does our working together as a group need to continue for people to move to the next levels of their healing?

How to know it's over if it's gone poorly:

• There has been damage done to the process that cannot be repaired.

• The process has fallen apart because participation has waned, or evaporated, or become toxic.

• The person who caused harm causes new harm while in the process.

• The survivor or the PWCH is no longer participating.

How to know it's over if things are stagnant:

Stagnation makes it is difficult to know whether and how to bring the process to a close. In this situation, the strength of a skilled facilitator/coordinator is key.

• Because not everyone has all of the information about the process, it can sometimes feel as though "nothing is happening" when, in fact, people are still working.

• A lot of this has to do with time.

• The survivor or the PWCH is no longer participating.

• People sometimes feel as though there's a ceiling on what they can accomplish and feel stuck. Sometimes facilitator or coordinator expectations are mismatched with the process.

• When someone violates agreements, processes can get stuck because people don't know how to get back on track.

• You can't figure out if you've been manipulated and by whom.

In general, the decision to close out a process is specific to each process. Sometimes this means a formal ending, such as a closing circle; sometimes you might meet individually with all parties; sometimes it's a final letter that summarizes all of the goals and if they were achieved. The important thing is to actually make it a point to end. Don't simply peter out.

Section C:
Technical Nuts and Bolts of CA Processes

1. Stitching It Together

The following two-page document is a summary of the *Creative Interventions Toolkit.*

It clearly lays out the steps to creating a CA process to address interpersonal violence. We share it here because people often ask for step-by-step descriptions of a process. There really isn't a uniform, step-by-step guide, but this document created by Philly Stands Up is an excellent cheat sheet.

We recommend making a copy of this to share with survivors and people who cause harm when you meet with them to discuss what a process entails.

We think that it's helpful for people to see how it can play out depending on the goals of the process.

///////////// QUESTIONS TO CONSIDER WHEN ORGANIZING A RESPONSE TO SEXUAL ASSAULT /////////////	*Getting Clear* • What is going on? • What kind of violence or abuse has happened or is happening? • Who is getting harmed? • Who is doing the harming?	*staying safe and sustainable* +What are risks and dangers right now? +Risks to whom? +What level of risk? + What are the risks & dangers if we take no action? +What are the risks & dangers if we take action? +Who needs safety & protection? +What plans can we make to provide safety & protection? +What do we need to do for self and community care? +Where are we vulnerable to burn-out?

supporting survivors/ bystanders	*goal setting*	*mapping allies and barriers*
• What violence or abuse did the survivor experience? • What harms have resulted? • What do they think will be helpful to them? • Who can best offer this support? • How are they getting ongoing support? • How are you taking care of yourself to provide that support?	• What do you want? • What do you not want? • What would you consider a success?	• Who can help? • Who can get in the way? • Who is in a good position to support the survivor? • Who is in a good position to offer support to the person or people doing harm? • Who can become an ally or become a better ally with a little bit of help? • What kind of help do they need and who can give it? • How can you draw on resources offered by organizations?

taking accountability	*working together*	*keeping on track*
• What concrete interventions could make the violence stop? • What could prevent further violence? • What are the points of leverage? How can they be used? • What milestones do you hope to reach? • What reparations are needed to promote survivor and community safety & healing?	· Who has the capacity to work on the process? · Is everybody prepared to use a harm-reduction model & meet people where they're at? · What identities & skills would be strategic to have on the team? · Does everyone know & agree with the goals? · How will you resolve disagreements? · What are their roles? ·How will you communicate & coordinate? · How will you make decisions?	• Are we ready to take the next step? • How did it go? • What did we achieve? • Did we celebrate our achievements (even the small ones)? • What needs to change? • What is the next step?

A community accountability process should never involve only one facilitator. It is essential that you have a tight team. There is an excellent section in the *Creative Interventions Toolkit (Section 3, pg. 5)* on the role of facilitators and how to be a good one. You can also look at the section in this workbook about the skills of effective facilitators.

Based on our experience over the years, we have found that having one person as the overall coordinator increases the likelihood for a successful process. This is especially true if you just have two teams, one to support the PWCH and one to support the survivor.

The difference between a facilitator and a coordinator:

Overall Coordinator	Team Facilitator
Designs the entire process	Co-designs the process for the team that they lead or are a part of (i.e. survivor team or PWCH team)
Has all of the information and decides which information to share across teams	Has information about the team they are on, and shares this with the coordinator, but not with the other team's facilitator, unless the coordinator agrees
In consultation with the other facilitators, the coordinator has the power to shut down the process if it is not working	Shares problems or blocks that arise on their team with the coordinator for support

Overall Coordinator	Team Facilitator
Approves all communication between parties and to the wider public/community, if needed	Works on statements or other writing that may be passed between parties
Facilitates meetings of all team members with the survivor and any circles	Facilitates team meetings

We recommend:

- 1-2 people to coordinate the entire process *(main coordinator)*
- 2-3 people to support the person who is responsible for the harmed *(facilitator)*
- 2-3 people to support the person who has been harmed *(facilitator)*

It is OK if the coordinators of the entire process are also on the support teams. However, the support team for the responsible party should not also be supporting the survivor and vice versa.

Once you have your team established:

1. Agree on some basic values that will hold your team together. If you are part of a collective, organization, or group, we recommend that you do this before an incident even occurs. Please keep these short and clear—no dissertations– think practice not theory. For example: "Survivor-centered means that we believe those who have been harmed," or, "We believe that people can transform and heal."

2. Agree on what information you will share with the entire team.

3. All information should always go back to the principal facilitators (even if you do not want the other support team to know the information).

4. Each team should meet separately and regularly to develop trust. It is important that no team undermines the other, and that all are working in the same direction. It's also best for the all teams to meet together to build trust and collaborate on critical points in the process.

5. The principal facilitator(s) should maintain careful boundaries. Be mindful of what information is shared between support teams. Only share information between teams that is essential to moving the process forward. It's essential that both teams trust you.

3. Effective Meetings are Key to Successful Processes

Don't set up meetings off the cuff. Effective meetings demand good preparation. Make sure that you clarify what you hope to accomplish, craft an agenda, recruit the participants, issue prework, and send out follow-up notes that detail key decisions and next steps.

Outside of general relationship building, meetings have three main purposes:

1. To inform and bring people up to speed.

2. To seek input from people.

3. To ask for approval.

Meeting Preparation Checklist

*Adapted from HBR Guide
to Making Every Meeting*

✓ Have you...

[ ] 1. Identified the specific purpose of the meeting?

[ ] 2. Made sure you need a meeting at all?

[ ] 3. Developed a preliminary agenda?

[ ] 4. Selected the right participants?

[ ] 5. Assigned roles to participants?

[ ] 6. Decided where and when to hold the meeting and confirmed availability of the space?

[ ] 7. Sent the invitation notifying participants when and where the meeting will be held?

[ ] 8. Sent the preliminary agenda to key participants and other stakeholders?

[ ] 9. Sent any reports or items needing advance preparation to participants?

[ ] 10. Followed up with invitees?

[ ] 11. Identified, if appropriate, the decision-making process that will be used in the meeting?

[ ] 12. Identified, arranged for, and tested any required equipment?

[ ] 13. Finalized the agenda and distributed it to all participants?

[ ] 14. Verified that all key participants will attend and know their roles?

[ ] 15. Prepared yourself?

Meeting Agenda

Meeting:	Date:
	Time:
	Location:
	Leader:
	Participants:

| Meeting Purpose:
(One Sentence) | Desired Outcomes:

1.

2.

3. |

| Meeting Agenda: | Time Allotted |
| Materials/Information Needed: | Person: |

4. Sample Contract for People Who've Been Harmed

Shira's example for people who've been harmed.

Agreements for working on your Community Accountability Process

My Commitments:

• I will hold your trust and keep all information that you share with me confidential. I may share important information with your whole team so that we are all on the same page.

• I will most likely make mistakes throughout our work together. I will be honest and open, and work to resolve all mistakes and keep your trust.

• I cannot guarantee that the person who harmed you will never harm anyone ever again. If you have questions or thoughts about this, I would love to talk more about why this is true.

• I will keep your healing at the center of our work together.

• I will support you in whatever ways I can while we are working together; however, I am not a replacement for a therapist.

• Because you are choosing to use CA (instead of the police), I will also keep the transformation of the person who harmed you at the center of our work together. If you have questions or thoughts about this, I would love to talk more about why this is a part of CA.

• I will work with your support team and serve as a coordinator between teams.

• I will be honest and open with you about the process and how it's going.

• I will design a process with your input, goals, and guidance. I will write down the process and explain it as many times as needed. The process may change as needed, and all changes will be discussed first.

• I will never discuss your process publicly without your knowledge or permission. I will never use your name or any identifying information.

• I will respond to emails or phone calls within 24-48 hours.

Your Commitments:

• I will find or remain in therapy or some kind of healing work throughout the CA process.

• I will work with Shira to define my goals for this process.

• If I have problems during the process with the CA process itself, or if Shira has made mistakes, I will use direct face to face or phone communication to resolve the problems.

• I can choose to end the process at any time. If I have decided to end the process, I will tell Shira and not leave her hanging.

• I will identify 1-2 people who I want to be on my support team and a part of the CA process.

• I will identify 1-2 people who I want to be my supporters who are not a part of the CA process.

• If I want to change the process, or have concerns about it, I will tell Shira.

• I will do my best to respond to emails or communication from Shira or my support team within 72 hours.

• I will give input on the design of the process.

• I will do the work (emotional, written, or otherwise) that I agree to do during the process.

All participants, including the support teams and the person who caused harm, agree not discuss the process on social media while it is ongoing or use social media as a weapon. If this happens, I understand that the process may not be salvageable.

Projected timeline for our work together:

Goals set by: _____/_____
Shira provides written process by: _____/_____
First check-in: _____/_____
First team meeting: _____/_____

More dates will be determined and written down once the process is decided together.

_____   _____
Shira Hassan   Name

Working Plans for Meeting with *XXX* and Support New York

Organization:
1. Meeting every 2-4 weeks at predetermined time
2. SNY keeps confidential notes on general items at meeting for their records.
3. SNY may assess the process with you either verbally or over email every 3 months (completely confidential).
   a. SNY's impressions of the process and your progress
   b. Your impressions of the process and the accountability group

Confidentiality:
1. Meetings are completely confidential. No details of what is discussed at the meetings will be disclosed to survivors, partners, or larger community until, if or when you and SNY decide to do so. We want meetings to be a safe space where you can think, talk and work out any issues without feeling watched or judged.
2. General information about the structure of the process, your attendance and cooperation, and SNY's impressions of your general progress may be disclosed.
3. At your request or the request of survivors or others invested in this process, we may discuss releasing information with consent from you and others involved.

Structure of Meetings:
1. SNY welcomes your input in developing the structure and content of the meetings.
2. We will analyze readings with a radical slant that focus on issues of sexual assault, abuse, patriarchy, gender, socialization, boundaries, power dynamics, etc., as well as how these larger ideas relate to our everyday lives.
3. We will talk about experiences, get to the root of why we act in oppressive ways and work to change those parts of ourselves.
4. We will think about how to connect our minds and bodies to regulate behaviors in moments of anger or hurt and curb abusive patterns.
5. These are just starting points and all of us should actively be thinking about how to form a productive process.

Professional Counseling:
1. We request that you attend regular counseling throughout the process. A list of free or sliding scale resources can be provided if you'd like.
2. The details of your counseling are completely confidential between you and your

2

counselor. We will not attempt to contact or gain information from your counselor. We do encourage you to discuss with us anything you wish to share.

Group Agreements:
1. No name calling, interrupting or aggressive language.
2. Be open to being challenged on oppressive perspectives, such as racism, sexism, or homophobia.
3. Be mindful of addressing any one person more than others (e.g., because of their perceived gender).
4. Treat everyone at the meeting as your and each other's equals.
5. Be willing to engage in readings and activities and take responsibility for your actions.
6. The purpose of these meetings is to deal with your behavior towards others and its impact. If you have issues you would like to address regarding the person who requested that you participate in this process, we ask that you seek another setting to deal with this such as counseling.

We are meeting because your actions have harmed someone else and created reverberations throughout your community. Our intentions are to examine the impact and origins of these behaviors, to understand the effect this has on others, and to take steps to avoid these acts in the future. This process may take time. Survivors and others in your community have been hurt, and at this time, people may not be comfortable with your presence in certain spaces, though with time and your effort this may change. Until then, please always be respectful when people set boundaries with you. If someone asks you to leave a space or says they don't want to talk about it, that's their right. People will respond when they are ready. Just try to be patient, think critically and be respectful.

Social media do's and don'ts for addressing harm

As social media has become increasingly popular, so has its use as a tool for disseminating information about harm and for seeking a form of accountability from those who harm. On its face, this appears to be a positive development. However, in some cases, social media itself has become a tool used to harm and to evade accountability.

Those of us who are engaged in community accountability (CA) efforts are wrestling with how to manage the impact(s), both positive and negative, of social media. The following words rely on advice and ideas from CA practitioners from across the U.S. It is a dynamic document that we hope will be adapted to each community that chooses to use it.

For those facilitating CA processes:

It's important within any CA process that participants create an overall communication plan (this should include social media). In general, you'll want to establish rules about how all parties will communicate with each other and with bystanders.

✓ Do's

Make social media agreements and messages as a part of your process. Consider what's needed for the safety of the harmed party and the transformation of the person(s) who caused harm.

What agreement(s) would you like to have around social media?

1. What can and can't be discussed?

2. Who is bound to abide by these agreements?

3. What are the consequences if the agreements are broken?

4. Who will be primarily responsible for ensuring that these consequences are implemented?

🚫 **Don'ts**

Act as though social media and the "real world" are distinct. They are not. What happens offline bleeds into the online world and vice versa. Do not minimize the impact(s) of online communication on community-building.

For individuals (bystanders and/or people directly involved in CA processes):

Slow down before posting. When we find out that someone in our community has raped, beaten up, or otherwise harmed someone we care about, all of our emotions get activated. We want to warn people; we want to get revenge for the person who's been hurt. We may want use social media to pressure the PWCH to participate in a CA process. We are also often coming from a place where we're thinking about ways we survived violence, or what people we love have survived without anyone showing up for them. Our adrenaline kicks in and makes us want to tell the whole world that the person who caused harm is a thief, rapist, abuser, etc.

But it's important to slow down. We should first ask, "What does the harmed person want or need?" They may be in shock or scared. They may need some time to figure out what they want or need, or they may have safety concerns.

Take the time to actually think about what justice would look like. What does the harmed person actually want to happen? This may take some time (not one day but weeks or months) to figure out. That's not a failure. It also may change over time.

Once you have that list of desired outcomes, ask yourself--and the survivor--how using social media might be helpful and useful or detrimental.

When you get some information, check it out. Twitter and social media in general are fast, which can be really useful. But also it's important to slow down and realize that a lot of stuff gets posted on social media and you may not have all the information about the situation.

✓ Do's

1. Consider some key questions before posting:

• If you are not involved in the process, what is your goal of public commentary?

• Have you considered the impact on the parties involved?

• Have you considered the impact on a positive CA process?

• Have you thought through consent? Social media can impact everyone involved—forever. So, before issuing your opinions through a venue that can permanently affect other people's lives, consider reaching out to the facilitator offline.

2. Take time to ask yourself, "Why am I sharing this? Is it about promoting a certain image of myself or hoping people see me in a certain way? Does it support healing and transformation, and how do I know that?"

3. If you are involved in the process, think about how it might the impact of people involved and consider consent. Have you talked this through with your support team or facilitators? Transforming harm requires vulnerability, which often requires a level of nuance and safety that is rarely possible through social media.

⊘ Don'ts

1. Judge a process in process.

As an outside person, there is no way for you to have a full perspective about what is going on. The impacted parties have placed time, trust, and care into working through this situation. Becoming judge and jury, without information, through social media is a form of harm in itself, and it replicates the values of the criminal legal system that we're attempting to transform.

2. Feel pressured to publicly intervene.

You ARE NOT obligated to offer public comments, especially about issues about which you have little to no information. It is unfair to be compelled to respond in a public way if you are uncomfortable, confused or otherwise unprepared to comment. Virtue signaling is not conducive to accountability processes.

3. When I see on social media that someone has hurt a person in my community or whom I know, I can SLOW DOWN and ask myself:

- How am I feeling? What does this bring up for me about prior experiences?

- What does the person who was hurt want?

- What are my motivations for posting about this on social media?

Note:

Just as is the case offline, social media "accountability" is often about shaming people to death. If you are engaging in online accountability with the idea that there is never any possibility of restoration, redemption or transformation, then you aren't actually engaging in transformative justice.

We're all just human, not perfect.

Tips for Navigating Public Calls for Accountability Online

1. Wait. You don't have to engage immediately unless someone is in immediate danger.

2. Have you inquired as to what this is about? What questions have you asked to gather necessary information?

3. We need to distinguish between how we treat people with whom we are in community and trust and others who have power over us and/or are strangers.

4. Geographic context: does it make sense to share public callouts from your location in city X if the parties involved live and work in city Y? What is to be gained?

5. Is this the only way to show support? What other ways might there be? Can you contact the person directly off social media?

6. Pick your battles – you do NOT need to have and/or give your opinion on everything.

7. Disagreements, even charged ones, can happen without a pattern of abuse being present. Are you able to differentiate between the two?

8. People are not one-dimensional targets; they are human.

9. Hold empathy for others. Don't enable conflict.

10. You can't shame or coerce people into accountability. It doesn't work.

11. You can invite people to participate in an accountability process. You should not coerce them. You cannot force them.

12. Beware of using the same strategies for every single situation.

13. Strategize offline with others, and show up online in a united way to support people being unfairly targeted.

14. *"Truths can be multiple and are revealed by the order of events."* — Sarah Schulman (p.65) | What is the originating action? What is the response?

15. Distinctions/context: a poster campaign might make sense for someone who raped you. Does it make sense to launch a poster campaign because you were disrespected by an event organizer? Posters are not a reasonable or effective response to emotional abuse or conflict.

16. Refuse to join the dogpile.

AREA 3

USEFUL ACTIVITIES TO TRY ON YOUR OWN, WITH YOUR TEAM, AND WITH CA PARTICIPANTS

Section A:
Activities for Facilitators

1. Journaling as Self-Care and Documentation

TIP: Keep a journal for self-care but also because documentation is very important.

Journaling and documentation are important aspects of good community accountability facilitation. A journal can be a tool for transforming personal problems, overcoming blocks to creativity, and expanding internal resources. The purposes of journaling can be manifold, helping you to set goals, develop self-knowledge and awareness, and sometimes even improve relationships.

Tips for Journaling

1. Get a roller pen; it writes more smoothly than a ballpoint pen.

2. Date every entry.

3. Don't edit yourself or your writing. Journaling is different than formal paper writing. Spontaneity is key in journaling. Don't let your inner critic inhibit you.

Some Journaling Techniques

1. **Creative list-making.** Start with a question like, "What do I want? What don't I want?" Make a chart.

2. **Dialoguing.** Person A talks to person B. These can represent two sides of you. It helps you engage in a conversation with yourself.

3. **Unsent letter.** You are writing a letter to someone you are angry at or someone whom you love but may not think it is a good idea to reveal yourself to. You may want to set a timer for 15 to 20 minutes so that you don't go on and on.

4. **Cathartic Writing.** This is writing that is done under intense emotion that calls for immediate release. Think of it as a process and not a product. Write the feelings that are flowing through you *(positive or negative)*. It can keep you from acting on intense emotions. It never hurts to wait until your emotions subside before proceeding to confront someone. An unsent letter can be a form of cathartic writing.

You want to MANAGE thoughts and feelings as a facilitator. You don't want to ERADICATE or STUFF or IGNORE them. People need a PAUSE or a SPACE for thinking and feeling safely.

5. **Descriptive Writing.** Most people think of this as journaling. This is a traditional diary. You might describe your day, for example.

6. **Free Intuitive Writing.** Relax and try to empty your mind. It's like emptying the trash. Follow your breathing as you write down words, drawings, and/or make collages.

6. **Reflective Writing.** Reflect on a session, issue, or situation, and contemplate it. You may ask yourself "why" something is as it is. You may look for the meaning and significance in an issue. You may look for particular patterns.

Prompts for your own journaling as a CA process facilitator. Meditate on the following ideas. Write/draw your thoughts or feelings.

• Do you believe that no one is disposable or expendable? Why or why not?

• "If you don't trust the people, they become untrustworthy." – *Lao Tzu, Tao Te Ching*

• "We realized we didn't know what we were doing, even the experts." *http://www.huffington-post.com/entry/how-we-learned-transformative-justice_us_58b2f41ce4b0780bac2a2f84*

Prompts for journaling with survivors and/or people who caused harm:

....

1. I only express my feelings when...

2. The only person who knows the real me is...

3. The biggest risk that I could ever take is...

4. A time people expected too much of me was...

5. I need to improve...

6. I escape my problems by...

7. What I need most from other people is...

8. What I like about me is...

9. I trust those who...

10. Compared to others I think I am...

11. Five years from now...

12. I only express my feelings when...

13. My day is happiest when I'm with...

14. Something I cannot tolerate is...

15. A past experience that will help me in the future is...

16. What would you like to see change in yourself during the process?

Suggested Reading: *Writing Down the Bones* by Natalie Goldberg

2. Dealing with Conflict

Conflict is normal in human relationships. In fact, it can be a driver of positive change. We sometimes/often need to change the way we relate to one another. One of a facilitator's unconscious expectations is about how people "ought" to handle conflict. Clearly, the format of CA processes implies a belief in talking matters over face-to-face, in taking responsibility, in moving beyond the past to emphasize "from now on." How did your own values and interests lead you to want to facilitate and/or coordinate CA processes?

1. Think about several conflicts you were in recently:

family dispute	problem with a friend or neighbor	problem at work or in the community

What did you do first? What else did you try? What worked? What might have worked? Which of the following do you always, sometimes, or never do in conflicts?

- Talk with a friend
- Avoid
- Speak directly to the person
- Hint at the problem
- Hit someone
- Arrange for a meeting
- Apologize
- Get visibly angry
- Take it out on someone else
- Go to an authority
- Use a go-between
- Write a note

- Ignore
- Complain to a third person
- Report to someone else who might do something
- Sulk
- Try to be reasonable
- Think of changing yourself
- Punch a pillow
- Leave, walk out
- Use your position of authority to assert control
- Make excuses
- Cry

What do your actions tell you about the way you prefer to deal with conflict? Will this make you more or less effective as a facilitator or coordinator?

2. Think about the ways your friends, family, co-workers handle conflict.

- Which ways do you find work well?
- Which ways make you angry?
- Which ways would you like to learn?

3. Remember a time you handled an uncomfortable situation well. What helped you prepare for that?

4. Have you developed your own way of de-escalating conflicts over the years? What are these? Write them down.

Do you have your own way of counting to ten? Be aware of what techniques work for you so you can be clear and relaxed during difficult moments in your facilitation.

Section B:
Activities for Survivors and People Who Caused Harm

Note

The following are **all activities**, however, the **activities with banners across the top** are specifically marked because they are formatted to be easily removed from this workbook and used as handouts.

Color Your Feelings

Color this spectrum with all of the emotions/feelings you've experienced since you were harmed.

Are there any emotions/feelings you haven't yet experienced?

Are there any emotions you have experienced that are not listed here?

Confused	Panicked	Anxious	Angry	Happy
Betrayed	Frustrated	Hurt	Guilty	Stressed
Tense	Calm	Relieved	Annoyed	Disappointed
Scared	Enraged	Excited	Insecure	Embarrassed
Sad	Content	Jealous	Lonely	Confident
Used	Disgusted	Vulnerable	Ashamed	Courageous

Activity 2: What's on your mind?

Materials

White paper (8.5 by 14 or 11 by 17)
Colored pencils or markers
Soothing music

Step 1
Play some soothing music in the background.

Step 2
Give a sheet of white paper to each person. Ask them to pick a pencil or marker.

Step 3
Ask each person to relax their mind, then SCRIBBLE on the paper in front of them.

(They shouldn't feel self-conscious about their scribbles. They don't need to do anything other than scribble. You might notice that some people will be hesitant about doing this. Encourage them to do what feels most comfortable.)

Step 4
Next, instruct participants to look at what they have scribbled, and to MAKE SOMETHING OUT OF IT. Can they SEE something in their scribbles on the page?

(Many people will complain that they can't make anything out of their scribbles. Encourage them to RELAX by closing their eyes and then opening them to look at their scribbles anew.)

Step 5
After they have MADE SOMETHING OUT OF THE SCRIBBLES, ask participants to TITLE their drawing.

Drawings have deep significance. They sometimes manifest what exists in our unconscious. Often what we draw represents core issues or concerns for us. Drawings can help us to surface buried anxieties or articulate particular feelings.

Step 6

On the back of the paper, or, if there is room, on the front next to the image, ask participants to engage in a JOURNALING exercise.

Ask them to begin by writing: I AM [title of their drawing]. From there, they can use stream of consciousness writing to describe what they want to say. Participants can use prompts like, "I feel... I wish... I think... I want..." if they get stuck.

Tell participants not to worry about grammar, spelling, or punctuation. Encourage them to use FREE ASSOCIATION. You can ask them to think about what they associate with their drawing.

You can tell participants that the image that they created must have some connection to them. Out of all of the images that they could have created, they chose to make the one they did – unconsciously.

> **When I (Mariame) first did this activity with a person who caused harm (PWCH), they ended up drawing a MASK from their scribbles.**
>
> **They wrote the following next to the image:** I am a Mardi Gras mask, I keep my thoughts to myself. I keep myself hidden. I feel like I brilliantly disguise the truth about myself and my feelings. I wear the mask that grins and lies.
>
> This is a line from a famous Paul Lawrence Dunbar poem that has always spoken to me. Why? Masks also make me think of my family and home (Africa). Always present in my thoughts and yet also so far away right now. I wear the mask that grins and lies.
>
> We had a really powerful conversation after this activity, and it became the basis of our entire talk session. Some images will really strike something. Others won't be as impactful. Tell participants that they can make this their own personal research project.
>
> Look up the significance of MASKS in different cultures, for example, or watch movies that have masks as a theme. Perhaps participants can begin collecting masks or taking pictures of masks. They can look for poems or other writings about masks.

Activity 3: Regrets, Hurts, Affirmations, Next Steps | Shira's Clearing Circle

Beginner level | Experience recommended
Size: 2-8 people
Time: 2-4 hours

I learned this circle from my mentor and lifelong teacher, Kelly McGowan. She offered it to me when I was working with a group that was stuck in complete crisis, and I was amazed at the results.

I have made some adjustments to the structure since that time, but kept the integrity and the purpose the same. The change that has worked best for me is the addition of an action plan. This circle method leads the participants towards a natural action plan, and I take the time to write it down and leave them with clear steps out of the stuckness.

This circle is best done with two to eight people, and takes between two and four hours, depending on the people present and their willingness to share.

As the facilitator, you should not plan to share during the circle, but instead hold the center of the circle. The second half of the circle requires tight facilitation. It is also best to plan a very short, "icebreaker"-style opening round.

This method is good for beginners; however, some experience with holding circles and facilitation is strongly recommended.

The central values I was taught and still use are:

1. Offer what you can

2. Ask for what you need

3. Pause — to listen, to stretch, to witness, to reflect — before speaking

4. Take care of the well-being of the group

Before the circle:

1. Get an understanding of the issue. Talk to everyone in the group to hear what they think is going on. Do not respond or share information between people. Simply hear all sides and take the time to listen deeply.

2. Decide if a circle will work. Not every issue is easily addressed by a circle. Circles require listening skills, time, and patience.

3. Remember that a resolution does not mean everyone leaves happy, or that everything is fixed. Sometimes it simply means the air is cleared for the next phase of work to begin. Sometimes it means that the group decides that they will no longer work together. This doesn't mean the circle failed. It often means it was successful, because the group was able to reach closure together.

4. Send the invitation. Invite each person to propose a date and time they can do and be sure that everyone knows what the circle is about and its purpose.

The Circle Method

This circle has four rounds. Each round allows people to talk without interruptions from anyone else present. I do not usually time each person unless I have to. It is best to discourage people from responding to each other during the circle; instead, they should speak from their own experience and use "I" statements.

The Four Rounds

Round 1
Hurts—each person in attendance has space to name what about the issue or subject has them feeling wounded, harmed, or "ouched."

Round 2

Regrets—each person speaks about something(s) they wish they had done differently that negatively impacted individuals or the situation.

These two rounds always come first. Depending on the interviews you did with each group member before the beginning of the circle, determine which of these rounds goes first. Participants often have an easier time accessing their truth if the circle begins with "regrets." However, beginning with "hurts" makes more logical sense to most, and I have most often facilitated the circle by starting with this round.

Break 15-20 mins

Round 3

Affirmations—each person names an appreciation for the group as whole (either for what was said during the circle, or wider appreciations). Note: many people may choose to say good things about some members and skip others—you may jump in as a facilitator to be sure that everyone is named. I always participate in this round of the circle in order to reflect the group's strengths.

Round 4

Action Steps—this space is used so that each person can name a step forward for the group. I tightly facilitate this section and often write ideas up with big paper. I include a timeline and ask the group who is responsible for each action step. The group is left with an action plan that they can immediately implement.

Box Activity

This is an awareness-building method that assists with perspective taking and communication skills. It is to be completed by each person involved after a conflict has occurred and persons involved have had a moment (if they need it) to settle down. If you are unable to come back together immediately after a conflict, it can be completed when you're reunited. Each person involved creates a narrative drawing from their own personal perspective.

Step 1
The story should begin (Box 1) from the moment you knew something was wrong and proceed horizontally through the boxes, like a comic strip, ending with the present moment or the moment that you felt okay again (Box 6).

Step 2
For each box, name an emotion you were feeling during that particular part of the conflict. You may either write the word for the emotion or draw it.

Step 3
When each person has completed their drawing, it is time to share and reflect. When sharing your story, it is helpful to use "I" statements and to make sure you're identifying a feeling for each part of the story.

Step 4
A share should be followed immediately by reflection from the other persons involved. When reflecting, it is important to use the same words the person who shared their story used.

For example, if they said "I felt scared when you yelled at me," You would say, "You felt scared when I yelled at you."

After each person shares and reflects, it's important not to force apologies or engage in blaming statements (for example, "Next time you should…").

To continue the conversation, consider asking questions like: "Is there anything that surprised you?", "Can you tell me more about that?", "What did you need?", etc.

· ·

Jane Ball learned this at a "mindful parenting" conference in a session lead by Erin Butterworth Hawkins, LCSW. She shared it with us as a tool for conflict resolution.

I knew something was wrong when... I felt _____	2 I felt _____	3 I felt _____
4 I felt _____	5 I felt _____	**In the present day...** 6 I feel _____

Activity 5: The Woodsman

The Woodsman (2004) offers insight into the role of isolation, social conditions, and public systems in increasing the likelihood of a re-offense, and the power of support and relationships in making transformation possible.

The film builds a case for transformative justice. It confirms our commitment to developing the capacity of our communities, families, and movements to make possible healing for those who have been violated, along with accountability and transformation for those who do offend. It highlights the role of bystanders and community in increasing the likelihood of both healing and transformation.

Mariame has used this film in processes with people who have caused harm. Specifically, she has asked people to watch it and then engaged in discussion about the film during a meeting with the PWCH.

Discussion Questions:

1. What were the conditions that triggered or increased the likelihood of Kevin Bacon's character's offending behavior?

2. What supported his transformation and increasing accountability and empathy?

3. What evidence was provided for this increase in accountability?

4. What vulnerabilities did you see in the children who were approached by offenders?

5. What made compassion possible for those who demonstrated it towards Kevin Bacon's character?

6. What support and education do families, workplaces and communities need in order to keep the community safe while increasing the possibility of offender accountability and transformation?

Activity 6: Anger Scale

A common feeling in conflict situations is anger. We all get angry, as survivors and facilitators. This activity is offered as a way to better understand and to transform anger.

Anger is both a feeling and a response. As a response, it is a 2-step process. First one experiences stress, and then there are trigger thoughts. Some of the trigger thoughts are: should – a set of rules in your head about how people "should" or "should not" act; and blame - acting as if the other person is solely responsible. We may interpret the other person's behavior in negative ways (irresponsible, uncaring, insensitive). We may confuse intent with impact.

Anger has several stages or levels of awareness (adapted from John Shuford):

1. **Annoyance** is a very slight hurt without any real conscious awareness *(e.g., someone brushes up against you while standing in line).*

2. **Irritation** is when we become consciously aware of the hurt and who or what is inflicting this hurt on us. We may try to remove ourselves from the situation, *(e.g., you are standing in line when that same person brushes up against you, and you glare at them and move away).*

3. **Anger** is when the hurt becomes real pain, and we usually focus our energy on one person. We mobilize our energy, resulting in a significant increase in physical tension. While still remaining in control, we try to solve the problem, often by directly confronting the person *(e.g., you are standing in line and the same person pushes you aside, then we push back and/or raise our voice and tell the person off).* The intention of anger is to change something.

4. **Rage** is when the pain becomes agony, and nothing else matters but stopping the pain or inflicting pain on the enemy. We are still in enough control to distinguish between friend and foe *(e.g., while you are standing in line this same person pushes you again, and you push back and physically or verbally assault them but others are able to stop the fight).* The intention of rage is to hurt the person inflicting pain on you. This can mean hurting a person physically, emotionally, economically, etc.

5. **Fury** is when the pain becomes unbearable and we are totally out of control; all of our energy is focused on the destruction of the perceived enemy, and we are unable to distinguish between friend and foe *(e.g., while standing in line, this same person pushes and challenges you again, and you totally lose control and physically assault the person with the intent of total destruction at any cost).* The intention of fury is to destroy. This can mean destroying someone physically, emotionally, economically. etc.

Ask people to brainstorm ways of dealing with discomfort or anger that don't hurt themselves or anyone else.

Three goals for dealing with anger:

1. Feel enough to pay attention to the message – pay attention to physical clues, pay attention to needs. Anger is information, like feeling a hot stove.

2. Channel anger to stay in control. For example, think of ten things you can do to handle anger that don't hurt yourself or anyone else. It is important to focus on the problem and your needs – not the other person and how they should change or behave differently.

3. Help the other person to do the same by listening to them and validating their feelings. Understanding is not agreeing.

Write a prayer for letting go of past hurts.

_____

_____

_____

_____

_____

_____

_____

_____

_____

_____

_____

_____

_____

When do you feel defensive? How do you defend yourself?

_____

_____

_____

_____

_____

_____

_____

_____

_____

_____

_____

_____

_____

How have you changed in the last 6 months? Year?
How do you feel about the change?

_____

_____

_____

_____

_____

_____

_____

_____

_____

_____

_____

_____

Describe and/or draw the place that you feel safest.

Do you feel connected to others today, or disconnected? What people, places, and activities help you stay connected? What people, places, and activities make you feel isolated?

_____

_____

_____

_____

_____

_____

_____

_____

_____

_____

_____

_____

List five ways you can be kinder to yourself.

1. _____

_____

2. _____

_____

3. _____

_____

4. _____

_____

5. _____

_____

What I've been told about me... _____

_____

_____

_____

_____

What I tell myself about me... _____

_____

_____

_____

_____

What I really know about me... _____

_____

_____

_____

_____

Section C:
Team-Building Activities

Activity 1: Five Habits to Cultivate in Your Accountability Teams

Care

- Being "for" one another
- Encouraging one another
- Coming alongside one another

Safety

- Having a "come-as-you-are" but not necessarily a "stay-as-you-are" culture
- Feeling safe enough to be yourself
- Accepting each other's faults and embracing strengths

Authenticity

- Being honest with each other
- Being truthful with yourself
- Taking relational risks with one another

Growth

- Spurring one another on
- Pushing each other to take growth steps

- Being willing to be transformed in the work
- Naming areas where growth needs to happen

Health

- Providing resources others may need
- Asking for help when needed
- Extending yourself in kindness

Activity

Lead your team in sharing one habit that most resonates with them and why. Practice authenticity as you share.

Facilitators should identify and periodically assess the team's needs according to the habits. How well is your group doing?

How to execute/actualize the habits?

Care

- Being listened to *(active listening)*
- Paying attention to group dynamics *(being attentive)*
- Encouraging each other *(being encouraging)*

Safety

- Checking in and asking, "How are we really doing as a group?"
- Identifying each other's strengths *(calling out the best in others)*

Authenticity

- Opening up to each other *(telling your story)*
- Giving and receiving feedback
- Owning your faults

Growth

- Dealing with team conflict
- Confronting others

Activity 2: Who You Are

Materials

White paper (8.5 by 11)
Pencils or pens

This exercise is often used at the onset of group formation. By the nature of its content, it's best used with a group where there will be more in-depth sharing.

Step 1
Each participant should get a sheet of paper and a pen or pencil. On the paper, the participants are asked to write their first name.

Step 2
Then, each person writes three adjectives which they feel describe them.

Step 3
After that, each participant fills in a response to the following four prompts:

I love _____
I fear _____
I hate _____
I long for _____

Step 4
Finally, each participant writes their last name.

An example of how this looks might be:

Shira,
I am funny, loving, creative;
I love my dog and friends;
I fear gossips and aggressive people;
I hate broccoli;
I long for more vacations at the beach,
Hassan.

This activity is a simple way to learn information about other group members. You must allow people to opt out of the activity. They should feel free to write or not to write.

Activity 3: When Everybody is a Survivor
—A Case Study

This activity has been adapted from a workshop that Lara Brooks created for Just Practice Training Calendar in Chicago. Shira has since adapted it for her social work students.

It is being offered here to help facilitators think through the following:

1. The role of mental health in Community Accountability practice

2. How to make mistakes in a process and recover

3. The long-term impact of CA processes in people's lives

4. How to sort through complex situations that are not cut and dry

This case study is a true story published with permission. It is an example from Shira's work that took place nearly 25 years ago and is riddled with mistakes and places where she missed the mark. The activity has been changed and taken out of a non-profit setting and is designed to be done with a group of people who you envision yourself working with on a community accountability process.

At the end of this activity there is a conclusion with a short reflection from Shira and more information about how all the participants are doing now.

We believe:

• We can and must end violence.
• Healing is possible.
• We need a model that isn't prisons and isn't police to keep our communities safe.
• This is hard work and it's a work in progress…it's on us to keep building the work.

Credit: API Chaya | Shared in the Transformative Justice track at the Allied Media Conference | June 2014

Learn more: www.apichaya.org

Directions:

1. Please read the case study all the way through. Please also look at all the questions that follow before you begin.

2. DO NOT READ the addendum at the end of this that reveals missing information about the individuals and how this concluded.

3. Assume that you have known all people in the story for about a year. Assume they are all telling the truth.

4. Assume the people you have called together to do this activity are members of an accountability team or squad. You have come together because you have been asked for help by someone in the story.

5. If you are stuck because you feel you do not have enough information—please just decide the answer for your group. Do not let a lack of information prevent you from finishing. For example, the gender of the participants is not included. Please decide the gender of the participants on your own.

6. After you have read the case study, please discuss it with your team.

7. Please answer as many of the questions as you can—however, answering ALL the questions is not essential. We are interested in how deeply you think something through, rather than how many questions you answer. Note the places you become stuck and come back to figure those out later.

Case Study:

You met Smush and Mystique as a couple. They both told you that they have been together for over a year. Smush is 20 years old and Mystique is 22. They have the same racial and ethnic identity and are from the same neighborhood. They both identify as queer.

They have been sleeping in an abandoned building for about 6 months. This squat is well known. Lots of other young people come in and out of the building and you have heard them refer to each other using street family labels.

You haven't heard of anyone who lives in the squat being arrested in a long time, even though the cops are always showing up there and doing "searches."

One day Mystique tells you they keep having dreams of being sexually assaulted. Mystique can't tell what's really happening and what's a memory. That same day, Smush comes up to you separately and tells you that they are worried about Mystique because they haven't been eating or sleeping through the night. Smush tells you that Smush was sexually assaulted by a police officer a few weeks ago while both Mystique and Smush were in their bed in the squat. The police officer assaulted Smush in front of Mystique who was hiding under the covers laying absolutely still while it was happening. Although Smush was the one assaulted by the officer, Smush felt that Mystique was in the most turmoil. You spend a few hours talking to Smush about being assaulted and about how to support Mystique. Smush does not want to report anything or go to the hospital. Mystique is aware that Smush has told you everything that happened with the police officer.

About a week later, Mystique comes to you with another member of the street family from the squat. Mystique tells you that Mystique thinks they have been sexually assaulted and that they hold Smush responsible. Mystique doesn't want to be anywhere near Smush and doesn't feel safe with Smush in any shared spaces. Mystique says if they see Smush that Mystique will call the police. You ask if they are both willing to meet together with you to talk everything through and decide next steps. They both agree.

The next day you show up to meet them both at a cafe and there are police outside. You get there in time to see Smush being arrested. Mystique tells you that they reported being sexually assaulted by Smush by calling 911.

Mystique tells you that they repeatedly warned Smush to stay away and that Smush kept showing up everywhere they went. Mystique says they have not slept for days.

Questions:

1. What environmental and social conditions led to a 911 call?

2. Who has power in this story and how do these conditions affect power?

3. Who are the players in this story?

4. How do you/the players intervene once 911 has been called? How do you support Smush? How do you support Mystique?

5. What would you do collectively to intervene in this incident as it is happening or change the story to shift who has power? What strategies would you use? What kinds of resources would you need?

6. Using all the frameworks discussed in this workbook, how would you and your team work to intervene? What would be your plan? How would you know if it worked?

7. What mistakes or mis-steps did Shira make? What would you do differently?

Use these questions to guide your intervention:

1. How do you engage those involved to address both of their experiences of violence?

2. What might accountability and transformation look like for all of the individuals impacted?

3. What role does mental health play in this situation? What additional resources or supports might you need to able to effectively assist both parties?

4. How do we connect young people with transformation/healing? Categorize according to short and long-term strategies.

5. What would your team do to prevent or transform the conditions that led to the situation in your community?

A month before...	*An hour before...*	*The following month...*
A week before...	*Later that day...*	*The following year...*
A day before...	*The following week...*	*Five years from now...*

Get magical! Maybe we don't have the resource today or right now, but let's dream the world we want to create.

Conclusion

As a community accountability practitioner, it is important to reflect on your experiences and notice your mistakes. This case study is one that has kept me awake over the years. I know both participants and still, 25 years later, I occasionally hear from them both. I have had the opportunity to acknowledge my mistakes and they have had the wisdom of hindsight and have offered me more information about what was happening for both of them during those days and weeks.

The biggest mistake I made was not contacting Mystique immediately after learning about what happened with the police officer. I did have a long conversation with Mystique when Mystique first told me that they were having dreams of being assaulted, but I was lost about how to sort through their experiences. In addition, the hour that we spent talking through their dreams was before I learned from Smush about the experience they both had with the police officer and I never followed back up with Mystique. I regarded Smush as the "primary survivor" and I think I was concerned about confidentiality and how to hold trust. The truth is that I really had no idea what to do.

Twenty-five years and a lot of reading later, I now know that Mystique was experiencing complex Post-Traumatic Stress symptoms. Mystique had survived childhood sexual assault and was deeply triggered by the experience of the police officer assaulting Smush right in front of them.

When I arrived at the café and saw Smush in a confrontation with the police officer, I panicked. I was not able to stop them from taking Smush, but I went to the police station and called a lawyer. When Smush was finally released, we learned they were not being charged because the police officers did not believe that someone with Smush's gender could "technically" (their words!) assault someone with Mystique's gender. I went with Smush to a friend's house and we stayed there together for a few days.

Mystique felt immediate regret when Smush was taken. A few days after Smush was released, we all met at the café. We talked for several hours and reviewed everything that happened. We met again 3 more times and I also met with each person separately for several months.

Mystique and Smush wound up staying together for about 5 more years after this incident. They have remained friends in community. In my last conversation with Mystique a few years ago, Mystique told me that they feel confident that Smush never harmed them and that they had been having flashbacks at that time.

Activity 4: Evaluation

Prompts

Praise
Something you love/appreciate

Ponder
A question you have

Polish
Something you think can be improved

Or

"I used to think…, but now I know…"

Resources

Resources

• Boyes-Watson, Carolyn. *Peacemaking Circles and Urban Youth: Bringing Justice Home.* St. Paul, MN: Living Justice Press, 2008)

• Boyes-Watson, Carolyn and Kay Pranis. *Heart of Hope: A Guide for Using Peacemaking Circles to Develop Emotional Literacy, Promote Healing and Build Healthy Relationships.* Boston, MA: Center for Restorative Justice, Suffolk University, 2010.

• Bumiller, Kristin. *In an Abusive State: How Neoliberalism Appropriated the Feminist Movement Against Sexual Violence.* Durham, NC: Duke University Press, 2008.

• Chen, Ching-In, Jai Dulani, and Leah Lakshmi Piepzna-Samarasinha, eds. *The Revolution Starts at Home: Confronting Intimate Violence within Activist Communities.* Cambridge, MA: South End Press, 2011.

• Critical Resistance (CR) Publications Collective. *Abolition Now! Ten Years of Strategy and Struggle Against the Prison Industrial Complex.* Oakland, CA: AK Press, 2008.

• Davis, Angela. *Are Prisons Obsolete?* NY: Seven Stories Press, 2003.

• INCITE! Women of Color Against Violence, ed. *Color of Violence: The Incite! Anthology.* Cambridge, MA: South End Press, 2006.

• INCITE! Women of Color Against Violence, ed. *The Revolution Will Not Be Funded: Beyond the Non-Profit Industrial Complex.* Cambridge, MA: South End Press, 2007.

• McCaslin, Wanda D., ed. *Justice as Healing: Indigenous Ways.* St. Paul, MN: Living Justice Press, 2005.

• Mogul, Joey, Andrea Ritchie, and Kay Whitlock. *Queer (In)Justice: The Criminalization of the LGBT People in the United States.* Boston: Beacon Press, 2010.

• Morales, Aurora Levins. *Medicine Stories: Essays for Radicals.* Durham, NC: Duke University Press, 2019.

• Morris, Ruth. *Stories of Transformative Justice.* Toronto: Canadian Scholars Press, 2000.

• Pranis, Kay. *The Little Book of Circle Processes: A New/Old Approach to Peacemaking.* Intercourse, PA: Good Books, 2005.

• Pranis, Kay, Barry Stuart, and Mark Wedge. *Peacemaking Circles: From Conflict to Community.* St. Paul, MN: Living Justice Press, 2003.

• Ptacek, James, ed. *Restorative Justice and Violence Against Women*. New York: Oxford University Press, 2010.

• Richie, Beth. *Arrested Justice: Black Women, Violence, and America's Prison Nation*. New York: NYU Press, 2012.

• Ross, Rupert. *Returning to the Teachings: Exploring Aboriginal Justice*. Toronto: Penguin, 2006.

• Russo, Ann. *Feminist Accountability: Disrupting Violence and Transforming Power*. New York: NYU Press, 2018.

• Russo, Ann and Melissa Spatz. *Communities Engaged in Resisting Violence*. Report of Women and Girls Collective Action Network, 2007. https://www.issuelab.org/resource/communities-engaged-in-resisting-violence.html

• Smith, Andrea. Conquest: Sexual Violence and American Indian Genocide. Boston: South End Press, 2005.

• Weingarten, Kaethe. *Common Shock: Witnessing Violence Every Day--How We Are Harmed, How We Can Heal*. New York: Dutton, 2003.

• Zehr, Howard. *Changing Lenses: Restorative Justice for Our Times*. Scottsdale, PA: Herald Press, 2015.

• Zehr, Howard. *The Little Book of Restorative Justice*. Intercourse, PA: Good Books, 2015.

Web-Based

• *Community Accountability // ideas, actions, art, & resources for communities responding to & transforming violence*
https://communityaccountability.wordpress.com/

• *Creative Interventions Toolkit: A Practical Guide to Stop Interpersonal Violence*
http://www.creative-interventions.org/tools/toolkit/

• *generationFIVE*
http://www.generationfive.org

• *Philly Stands Up*
http://www.phillystandsup.com/resources.html

• *Bell Bajao - "Ring the Bell" Campaign*
https://en.wikipedia.org/wiki/Bell_Bajao

- *Stop It Now*
http://www.stopitnow.org/

- *Storytelling and Organizing Project*
http://www.stopviolenceeveryday.org/

- *Transform Harm*
https://transformharm.org

Trauma and Recovery

- Bass, Ellen and Laura Davis. *The Courage to Heal: A Guide for Women Survivors of Child Sexual Abuse.* New York: William Morrow Paperbacks, 2008.

- Bass, Ellen and Laura Davis. *Beginning to Heal: A First Book for Men and Women Who Were Sexually Abused As Children.* New York: William Morrow Paperbacks, 2003.

- Chang, Joe, Wang Wei-dong, and Jiang Yong. *The Treatment of PTSD with Chinese Medicine--An Integrative Approach.* Beijing: People's Medical Publishing House, 2010.

- Gartner, Richard. Beyond Betrayal: Taking Charge of Your Life After Boyhood Sexual Abuse. Hoboken, NJ: Wiley, 2005.

- Grubman-Black, Stephen. *Broken Boys / Mending Men: Recovery from Childhood Sexual Abuse.* Caldwell, NJ: The Blackburn Press, 2002.

- Harris, Maxine. *Trauma Recovery and Empowerment: a Clinician's Guide for Working with Women in Groups.* New York: The Free Press, 1998.

- Herman, Judith. *Trauma and Recovery: the Aftermath of Violence -- From Domestic Abuse to Political Terror.* New York: Basic Books, 2015.

- Hunter, Mic. *Abused Boys: The Neglected Victims of Sexual Abuse.* New York: Fawcett Columbine, 1990.

- Jensen, Derrick. *A Language Older Than Words.* White River Junction, VT: Chelsea Green Publishing Company, 2004.

- Levine, Peter. *Waking the Tiger: Healing Trauma.* Berkeley, CA: North Atlantic Books, 1997.

- Singer, Ken. *Evicting the Perpetrator: A Male Survivor Guide to Recovery From Childhood Sexual Abuse.* Holyoke, MA: NEARI Press, 2010.

• Watkins, Mary and Shulman, Helene. *Toward Psychologies of Liberation.* Bakingstoke, United Kingdom: Palgrave Macmillan, 2008.

• Weingarten, Kaethe. *Common Shock: Witnessing Violence Every Day--How We Are Harmed, How We Can Heal.* New York: Dutton, 2003.

• Van der Kolk, Bessel A. *The Body Keeps the Score: Brain, Mind, and Body in the Healing of Trauma.* New York: Penguin Books, 2015.

• Van Dernoot Lipsky, Laura with Connie Bark. *Trauma Stewardship: An Everyday Guide to Caring for Self While Caring for Others.* San Francisco: Berrett-Koehler Publishers, Inc., 2009.

Afterword

> "Everything is connected...no one thing can change by itself."

—Paul Hawken

Our interdependence means that we are each other's tormentors but also each other's healers. CA processes are intended to help address harms that cause suffering in people's lives. They are, at their best, an opportunity to resolve our hurts with others.

This workbook is the product of years of practice and incorporates learning from all of our teachers. Our most important teachers have been the people who have trusted us with their pain and chosen to embark on CA processes to address various harms.

Several people who are also our teachers and our comrades took time to read this, offer their feedback, and helped to make this project a reality. In particular, we thank Rachel Caidor, Tanuja Jagernauth, Mimi Kim, Erica Meiners, Mia Mingus, and Leah Lakshmi Piepzna-Samarasinha. Thanks too to our comrades Deana, Keisa, Rachel and Ana who worked alongside us as part of the Just Practice Collaborative and encouraged us to create this workbook. Gratitude to Vita Eya Cleveland, Lindsey E. Jones, and Eva Nagao for their help with editing. Thanks also to the Open Philanthropy Project for subsidizing a retreat which gave us valuable time to outline this workbook and for covering the costs of editing and designing the project. We extend our gratitude also to Molly Costello and Rachel Hoffman for their design work which has made this workbook so accessible and beautiful.

We offer this workbook with humility, cognizant that there is a lot we don't know and cannot adequately express. It is always nerve-racking to put something out into the world because it will be inevitably judged and criticized. The alternative, however, is to simply hoard whatever knowledge and information we've gleaned from our work out of trepidation. That would be a shame, we believe. So--here's our offering, with all of its imperfections. We send it out in the world knowing that it is just one tool, and we hope that it will be of use.

We end with Audre Lorde's words, which we find always relevant to our work:

Audre Lorde

There is a world in which we all wish to live. That world is not attained lightly. We call it future. If, as Black Feminists, we do not begin talking, thinking, feeling ourselves for its shape, we will condemn ourselves and our children to a repetition of corruption and error. It is not our destiny to repeat white America's errors, but we will, if we mistake its symbols for success.

We welcome your feedback at transformharm@gmail.com. Let us know if you have suggestions and/or want to let us know how you've used this workbook.

Fumbling Towards Repair

A Workbook for Community Accountability Facilitators

Mariame Kaba & Shira Hassan